A THEATRE OF MACHINES

A THEATRE OF
MACHINES

A. G. Keller

THE MACMILLAN COMPANY

NEW YORK

© 1964 by A. G. Keller
Printed in Great Britain by
Jarrold & Sons Ltd,
Norwich

First published in the United States by
The Macmillan Company, 1965

Library of Congress Catalog Card No. 64–13773

TO MY WIFE

LIST OF PLATES

with corresponding text on opposite page

	Introduction	*page* 1
1	Clockwork mill (*Ramelli, Le Diverse et Artificiose Machine, pl. 131*)	12
2	Paper-mill (*Strada, Kunstliche Abriss, aller handt Wasserkunsten, pl. 100*)	14
3	Pump with crankshaft (*Strada, pl. 76*)	16
4	Elevator with endless chain (*Ramelli, pl. 139*)	18
5	Collapsible and mobile bridge (*Ramelli, pl. 143*)	20
6	Expanding bridge (*Ramelli, pl. 147*)	22
7	Pump with Archimedean screw (*Ramelli, pl. 46*)	24
8	Watermill (*Ramelli, pl. 115*)	26
9	Watermill (tubmill) (*Besson, Livre Premier des instruments mathématiques et méchaniques, pl. 28*)	28
10	Watermill with reversed Archimedean screw (*Branca, Le Machine, pl. 19*)	30
11	Hydraulic spinning-wheel (*Branca, pl. 20*)	32
12	Calender (*Zonca, Nuovo Teatro di Machine et Edificii, p. 56*)	34
13, 14	Multiple spinning mill (*Zonca, pp. 68, 74*)	36, 38
15	Spring-driven spit (*Scappi, Opera, pl. 19*)	40
16	Horizontal windmill (*Verantius, Novae Machinae, pl. 10*)	42
17	Smoke-jack spit (*Zonca, p. 91*)	44
18	Smoke-jack coining mill (*Branca, pl. 2*)	46
19	Roller-press (*Zonca, p. 76*)	48
20	Rolling and slitting mill for lead strips (*Zonca, p. 79*)	50
21	Pumps for well (*Ramelli, pl. 2*)	52
22	Pumphouse (*Ramelli, pl. 9*)	54
23	Ornamental fountain with automata (*Ramelli, pl. 186*)	56
24	Pumps for drainage (*Ramelli, pl. 100*)	58
25, 26	Mitre locks (*Zonca, pp. 9, 12*)	60, 62
27	Slipway (*Zonca, p. 58*)	64
28	Revolving crane (*Ramelli, pl. 176*)	66
29	Two-way winch for artillery (*Ramelli, pl. 189*)	68
30	Inclined ox-mill (*Zonca, p. 26*)	70
31	Targone's mobile mill (*Zonca*)	72
32	Hand-mill (*Ramelli, pl. 129*)	74
33	Amphibious armoured car (*Ramelli, pl. 152*)	76
34	Carriage with equilibrated suspension (*Besson, pl. 17*)	78
35	Dredger's trident for removing rocks (*Besson, pl. 20*)	80
36	Dredging shovel (*Verantius, pl. 41*)	82
37	Apparatus for raising wrecks (*Besson, pl. 58*)	84
38, 39	Screwjack (*Ramelli, pls. 155, 156*)	86, 88
40, 41	Wrenches (*Ramelli, pls. 157, 158*)	90, 92
42	Reading machine (*Ramelli, pl. 188*)	94

43 Instrument for keeping the feet warm (*Scappi, pl. 22*)   *page* 96
44 Automatic fan (*Strada, pl. 50*)   98
45 Fire engine (*Besson, pl. 52*)   100
46 Sawmill (*Besson, pl. 14*)   102
47 Pump with endless chain (*Strada, pl. 62*)   104
48 Tide-mill (*Verantius, pl. 17*)   106
49 Funicular bridge (*Verantius, pl. 36*)   108
50 Lever-driven ship (*Besson, pl. 60*)   110
51 Diving bell and diving suits (*B. Lorini*, Delle Fortificatione, *p.204*)   112
52 Parachute (*Verantius, pl. 38*)   114

Plates number 15, 34, 48, 49, 51 and 52 are reproduced by permission of the British Museum; all other plates by permission of the Cambridge University Library.

INTRODUCTION

I

WHAT IS IT THAT DISTINGUISHES OUR CIVILIZATION FROM THOSE THAT HAVE PRECEDED it? Most people, I suppose, would think first of the rich treasury of mechanical devices at our disposal; they might speak of the Industrial Revolution, of a technology which, after conquering the Earth's surface, is now reaching up into the skies. Ours is a mechanized society, and it has been the machinery of western Europe which, sometimes violently, sometimes by more insidious subversion, has overthrown all other cultures, civilized and savage alike, and reconstructed them in the European image. Perhaps we might prefer to point to other distinguishing marks of modern society as being more idealistic; our scientific research or our democratic way of life. Even so, mechanization has been all-important in providing both the tools and the inspiration for scientific research, and also the materials of modern affluence on which democracy is based – rapid communications, cheap and abundant goods.

If this is so, it seems a pity that the origins of this movement of mechanization have been so neglected, and the achievements of its earlier phases so ignored. At school we all learned of the Industrial Revolution – of Watt watching his kettle, of Stephenson and his *Rocket*, of Crompton's mule and Arkwright's loom. Everything before them was supposed to be sunk in the darkness of slavery and serfdom; only Leonardo da Vinci stood out, as the 'inventor' of aeroplane, submarine, and anything else you can think of, and he had to conceal his wonderful discoveries in mirror-writing for fear that the Inquisition would find out and carry him off to be burned at the stake as a wizard.

The truth is that the Industrial Revolution was no sudden affair. The realization that it was affecting the whole of society from top to bottom may have been sudden, but the revolution in technology was actually a very long process, advancing slowly over several centuries and only gradually gathering impetus. During the past few years there has been a growing interest in the technical progress of the Middle Ages. Although the power of water has been utilized in several other civilizations, it was nowhere exploited so widely as in medieval Latin Christendom, where, almost as soon as the fog of the Dark Ages lifted, the waterwheel, soon to be applied to a score of other industrial purposes, could be found grinding corn in almost every parish. Where water was not available, the wind often served in its place, and in many areas the windmill became as familiar a part of the landscape as the church spire. Professor Bertrand Gille of the University of Clermont, who has done much to make us aware of this process, has with justification described the use of waterpower as 'the industrial revolution of the Middle Ages'.

A fairer appreciation of the achievements of the Middle Ages has tended to devalue the glories of that intermediate period which, for want of a better word, we call the Renaissance. Deprived of true modernity by the modernists, and regarded as a decadence of the real Middle Ages by the medievalists, the period from 1450 to 1650 comes in for derogatory remarks by both parties. Yet between the sowing and the harvest there is an important if undramatic stage which should not be ignored. In the history of the mechanized society the Renaissance (and especially the latter part of the sixteenth century) is the time when the tender plant first appears above the surface. A few imaginative and inventive minds set out to show their contemporaries the potentialities of machinery, and a number of attentive ears heard their message and spread it abroad. The initiative of ingenious but illiterate artisans had in the past failed to attract the notice of the leaders of society; a gentleman or a scholar might accept the products of their skill, but it was felt that he should not concern himself unduly with their activities. But now we begin to find monarchs practising their own mechanical ingenuity and fostering it among their subjects, and scholars, in order to feel less overshadowed by the glories

I

of antiquity, drawing confidence from technical achievements. Just as dabbling in mechanical inventions became respectable for the upper classes, so the artisans themselves, much more given to reading than their ancestors, were readier to look for theoretical explanations for their work and to expect an improvement in their lot from a knowledge of 'the mathematics' – even if that knowledge was restricted to a smattering of Euclid, as it normally was.

It was at this crucial moment in the history of our technology that a number of books appeared, devoted to making a wider public conscious of the benefits which better machinery could give them, while showing the artisan how important it was to apply theoretical considerations to machines, as opposed to merely putting them together by rule of thumb. We must not suppose that the inventions depicted in these books were themselves very revolutionary. The important thing is not so much to do something as to do it consciously and to see where it is leading to. There are three books of mechanical inventions which have a special importance for their contribution to this new consciousness. They are Jacques Besson's *Livre des Instruments Mathematiques et Mechaniques*, with sixty plates, which appeared in 1571–2; Agostino Ramelli's *Diverse et Artificiose Machine*, containing nearly 200 plates, certainly the richest and most thorough, which came out in 1588; and Vittorio Zonca's *Teatro Nuovo di Machine et Edificii*, the most sober and realistic, published at Padua in 1607. By devoting a whole book entirely to pictures of machines, the authors gave a comprehensive view of the sort of advance they thought possible, while in their prefaces and descriptions they showed the mechanical theory on which their ideas were based.

Besides their great historical interest, these books are often very attractive aesthetically. Although the workshop was new territory for most of the illustrators, they succeeded in producing pictures at once pleasing to the eye and precisely accurate in their descriptions of the machine with all its parts. Surprisingly, although illustrations drawn from these books can sometimes be found in general histories of science and technology, usually much reduced in scale, no one has ever re-published them, and this wealth of fascinating material remains known only to a handful of scholars, accessible only in the original editions in the great libraries. This book, then, is an anthology of Renaissance machines, made up of a selection of the most interesting plates from the three major books as well as from a number of minor ones, some of the plates being selected on the ground of their attractive appearance, some for their boldness of imagination, and others for their importance as the crude early forms of what were later to prove important inventions.

The books of Besson and his successors were the first published works devoted to machinery and its possibilities. But they were not the first to design improved machines or to make collections of mechanical drawings. Ancient Greek and Roman traditions had not been totally hostile to machinery. The influence of Vitruvius' great compendium on architecture, which contains a number of machines, pervades all the writings of Renaissance engineers, and many engines for raising water and lifting or drawing weights were inspired by those he describes. Many ancient books on the art of war contain descriptions, often illustrated, of the war-machines of Roman and Hellenistic armies, and they were read attentively by our authors; and there was also a vogue at the time for the strange and ingenious devices and experiments of Hero of Alexandria, which are based on the suction or compression of air and water.

A number of sketch-books and notebooks, describing various machines, have survived from the later Middle Ages. The earliest surviving collection is that of a French architect, Villard de Honnecourt, from the mid-thirteenth century. There is, of course, no reason to suppose that he was unique in his generation; he only had the good luck to survive. Indeed, so far only a few of the great libraries of Europe have been properly scoured for technical manuscripts, and it may well be that others will turn up in the course of time. As the Middle Ages drew to a close, these sketch-books became more common; we have more for the fifteenth century than the fourteenth, still more for the early sixteenth century. Leonardo da Vinci towers above the others by his breadth of vision and the universality of his interests. He was great, but not always completely original; indeed, he is known to have annotated a mechanical manuscript by his older contemporary, the Sienese engineer Francesco di Giorgio.

For more than a century after the invention of printing in the West, nobody considered publishing these sketches. Their authors might not have felt it necessary to take the extra precaution of describing their designs in mirror-writing like Leonardo, but they were strongly inclined to keep their discoveries to themselves. In a world which knew little of copyrights or patents, the inventor had no interest in publicizing his work for others to steal. So long as their secrets remained secrets they were valuable, but once they became public property they were worthless. No wonder that few 'inventors' were prepared to expose their brain-children to the critical judgement of their peers.

Even so, a patent system was beginning to grow up. Monarchs had less interest than the inventors in keeping inventions private, and they were ready to grant privileges of copyright as their ancestors had granted lands, making the reproduction of specified inventions illegal for a space of several years. Protected in this way, mechanicians might have begun to think it worth the risk of telling the world of their discoveries in books. They might also have been influenced by the growing market for books of mathematical instruments, which could have taught them that publicity was as good a servant as secrecy. The traditional idea was to seek a patron, the more elevated the better. The king was the fount of all honour, and it was the dream of every bright fellow with an original idea, be it a wonderful engine or a plan to sail across the ocean to the Indies, to sell that idea to his monarch, and so make his fortune basking in the sun of royal favour. Gradually the notion took hold that your fellow-citizens were as rich and powerful in the aggregate as any monarch, and publishing a book was an excellent way of catching their attention.

During the Renaissance the old teachers of the abacus were blossoming out into a new profession, the mathematical practitioners. Besides teaching mathematics they also made mathematical instruments, a trade which was now becoming more important than the teaching side of the profession. The reasons for the growing demand for the instruments of navigation in the sixteenth century are obvious. But there was also a demand for instruments by surveyors, architects, and miners. The old rule-of-thumb methods were felt to be inadequate; greater precision was now demanded and precise instruments of calculation were needed to attain it. The mathematical practitioners, a new profession, had no guild to protect them. Literate without being scholars, they had to make their own way, and, often moving from place to place in search of pupils, they felt a need to advertise their presence. And what better way than by inventing a *new* mathematical instrument? So the book fairs were flooded, from the 1530's on, with holometres, mecometres, pantometres, and even Henry-metres (not, however, to measure Henrys) – all-purpose instruments of calculation in rich variety. Jacques Besson had led a career of this type, as a wandering teacher of mathematics, and one of his earlier books is devoted to the 'cosmolabe', a mathematical instrument to end all mathematical instruments and of incredible complexity; flexible, too, so that it could be adjusted into as many positions as a modern desk lamp. It may be that the success of these books of instruments gave Besson the idea of publishing his machines, too, for at least one of these instrument-makers, Abel Fullon, like Besson a French Protestant, promises in the preface to his *Holometre* all sorts of other wonderful 'machines, engines, movements, metal-casting and other such inventions' to follow. However, he was murdered before he had a chance to publish them.

Perhaps Besson was also inspired by the great success of Georgius Agricola's famous work on metallurgy, *De Re Metallica*, which had appeared a few years before. Agricola was a physician working in the mining regions of south Germany, and his book was intended to cover all aspects of the extraction and preparation of metals. But the sixth book, which deals with the machines used in mines for pumping out water, ventilating the shafts, and hauling up the ore, is the most lavishly illustrated section of the whole work, and it seems to have caught the attention of the public more than the books which deal more strictly with the nature of the various metals and how they are to be worked. Indeed, he is sometimes treated primarily as the author of a book of machinery, and he is quoted by several of the later writers on machines.

However much people might be impressed by Agricola's machines, they did not originate in the mines, and their use was not confined to them. Only much later did the mine become 'the front-line of technology', and the pumping of mines a major problem. In the age of Besson, Ramelli, and Zonca, the vanguard of technical advance still marched, as it had done since antiquity, under the ensign 'Architectura'. The most cursory examination of any Renaissance book of machines shows an imbalance that seems to us very curious: pumps and cranes *ad nauseam*, but transport and textiles very skimpily treated; little metallurgy and less agriculture; several important trades, such as the various branches of ceramics, completely ignored. The reason is clear: engineering and mechanics are the children of architecture and apply themselves first and foremost in her service.

The Renaissance inherited the ancient tradition that architecture is the Queen of the Arts, comprehending and organizing all the others. A gentleman, even a prince, would not feel himself demeaned if he studied it, and a scholar could apply himself with relish to the mathematical problems involved, especially in the classical style of architecture. The architect, after all, does not dirty his hands, he just supervises the work of others, looking on and giving orders – a noble occupation. The Ancients had a high respect for architecture, and the ruins of their buildings were the chief visible signs of the glory of their civilization; the study of them was a fitting occupation for any man. So it is not surprising to find that Renaissance dreams of the marvels of antiquity put on an architectural dress.

If architecture was open at the top, so to speak, it was nearly as open at the bottom. There was no guild of architects to check entry and control practice, no apprentice architects learning their trade. In fact, it was common for the great architects of the Renaissance to start off as carpenters, masons, painters or goldsmiths. A man could not describe himself as an architect until he was already quite high up in his profession, and there was no regular organization to trammel initiative, as often happened in other trades. Architecture became a way up in the world for young men engaged in any of the plastic arts. This had been partly true even in the Middle Ages; but the master-masons who built the great cathedrals then had not the prestige of the sixteenth-century architect.

Architecture at that time meant far more than it does today, for it included all that we now understand by the term 'engineering'. The word *ingeniarius* makes its first appearance in the later Middle Ages – a maker of *ingenia*, simply ingenious devices, usually military. In the Renaissance we also find it for one who specializes in designing fortifications. But throughout our period the two terms remain interchangeable, and all our authors could lay just claim to either title. A man might specialize in some branch of architecture, might be a millwright, a 'conductor of waters', or a master of ordnance and fortification, but he was usually ready to turn his hand to more conventional types of architectural work if need be.

The most highly developed of these branches of architecture was what we should now call hydraulic engineering. Perhaps the current architectural fantasies had something to do with it. Were not the water-gardens of Renaissance Italy inspired by the desire to realize this wonderland in tangible reality, with its fountain-jets and moving statues, its hydraulic organs and artificial waterfalls? All this demanded that the garden be supplied with a powerful head of water, which often had to be pumped up from quite a distance. The waterworks at Marly, which helped to supply the fountains of Versailles in a later generation, were the wonder of their age – perhaps the greatest and most complex achievement of the old hydraulic engineer. Of course this aesthetic and imaginative demand for fountains in the gardens of great lords was not the only reason why waterworks were regarded as an important part of the architect's work. From time immemorial, certainly before the great empires of antiquity and right through the Dark Ages after the collapse of Rome, men have been slowly pushing back the wasteland, and in many places in Europe, especially northern Italy and the Low Countries, the wasteland means the marshes. In Italy, if some districts have too much water, others quite close may suffer from a lack of it through the long months of summer, and so we read of drainage and irrigation all through the Middle Ages, here a patch of land and there a patch, drainage-ditches growing into small canals, dikes growing ever higher, networks of channels carrying water to dry fields. By the middle of the sixteenth century the rewards of labour were beginning to show, in the wealth and prosperity of the best-drained and irrigated lands.

'So you see the clear waters flowing on every side in their proper conduits or canals, in such fashion that in some places three or four canals are to be seen, constructed one upon the other with great ingenuity to carry the water higher or lower, according to the situation of the fields, a thing certainly marvellous to think upon, and most useful. Whence the hay is cut here three or four times a year, and sometimes five, as happened in 1532: and so much milk is taken from the cattle, to make cheese, that they make such cheeses as might seem almost incredible to those who have not seen them. Whence in 1531 there were four cheeses, or 'forms' as they say, of fantastic size, made by order of Giovan Francesco, count of Somaglia, and each of them weighed 500 pounds. Truly a thing marvellous to think upon . . .', writes Leandro Alberti in his Italian guide-book, published in 1550. An increasing population in the country needed water for irrigation; an increasing population in the towns needed it for drinking; meanwhile, the rival demands of different industries for waterpower, to drive the wheels of flour-mills and fulling mills, foundries and sawmills, pressed hard upon the resources of even the best-watered lands. So it is not surprising to find that pumps and engines for raising water hold the first place in our books. Essentially they are all derived from the types already found in antiquity and described by Vitruvius in his book on architecture: the chain of pots, the tympanum or 'drum-wheel', the suction-pump, the Archimedean screw; one way or another, these are the sources for all the countless subtleties and variations to be found in our books.

Another important field for the engineer was the war-machine. The old catapults and trebuchets were fast disappearing in the Renaissance, but the ardent mechanician still had plenty to test his wits on. The modernizing army with its demand for speed provided him with fresh opportunities, in designing collapsible bridges and scaling-ladders, and simple handy devices, easily transportable, to be used in emergencies. Mobile hand-mills were much in demand, so were engines for raising weights, lifting up fallen cannon or damaged baggage-wagons, or clearing spoil from trenches and moats. The up-to-date engineer carried his own mathematical instruments and other 'beautiful secrets' about with him, and often a few jacks and wrenches and machines for breaking and entering postern-gates and portcullises. Descriptions and illustrations of these engines often found their way into the abundant literature on the art of war, partly in accordance with the tradition of those ancient writers on the subject who had devoted a chapter to *machinae bellicae*, partly to advertise the authors' own specialities (they all had one). Since the art of war was so much more noble than the money-grubbing mechanical arts of peace, kings and great magnates first gained an interest in the subject from these books. The chapters on military machines began to grow, new machines made their appearance, books were devoted specifically to the subject, and soon machinery and its improvement began to be of interest to a wider, socially more important public than the artisans. The eccentric genius, with his pocket full of crazy but ingenious plans for wiping the enemy off the face of the earth, is not a creation of modern times: there was no lack of them in England in the 1580's and 1590's, pestering the councillors of Queen Elizabeth I.

If engines for pumping water and for use in war take the lion's share of our mechanical inventions, we should not pass over a third important type, the machines 'whereby a great weight is raised by a small force'. The sketch-books of the earlier fifteenth- and sixteenth-century engineers are full of variations on the theme of crane, hoist, and traction-engine. No doubt there was a practical problem here. The architects who built the great churches, halls, and palaces of medieval and Renaissance Europe had not the limitless resources in manpower of the ancient empires. If a single town, rich but not perhaps very large, wished to build a cathedral or a town hall that would enable the citizens to look their rivals over the mountain in the face, there would have to be some economies somewhere, and ingenuity in the raising of blocks of stone to lofty Gothic pinnacles would eliminate the need for and the expense of maintaining legions of unskilled heavers on ropes, such as were needed to build the temples of ancient Egypt.

Some of these labour-saving devices were perhaps the invention of medieval Europe, for manuscript illuminations show winches turned by cranks, and flywheels steadying the revolutions of their axles; while up on the scaffolding of the rising building small cranes haul up the stones, or else a gibbet holds a pulley free of the work, so that the material can be handled more easily. Other devices, and these the basic ones – windlass, pulley, lever, and screw – the medieval masons inherited from the ancient Greeks, who had suffered similar difficulties, although to a lesser degree, since they did not build so high as Gothic architects. Greek mechanics too had an architectural background. The Greeks defined mechanics as 'the art of raising weights', and it would seem that their scientific tradition, expressed in the writings of Aristotle, Archimedes, and Pappus, and no less in the legends of Archimedes and his wonderful machines, pushed the Renaissance mechanicians towards similar problems, much more than might have been strictly warranted. They were fascinated by the immense potentialities, as they supposed, of the advantages to be won by the multiplication of mechanical powers, without being quite sure what they could do with them once they had got them.

Certainly the ancient writers were never quite so overwhelmed by these potentialities. This may be partly due to the subtleties which the later Middle Ages introduced in the way of transmission of power: complex trains of gears, and systems of pulleys and drums driving one another through cable-belts or chains had once been confined to the intricate mechanisms with which men like Hero of Alexandria had amused their patrons. But it was the water-powered industries of the Middle Ages which made them a thing familiar to every carpenter and smith. Several important methods of the transmission of power were entirely new. Crank-handles and flywheels have already been mentioned; several more could be added, multiple crank-shafts, rocking beams, conical whims, ratchet-bars, and 'ladders' engaging in sprocket-wheels.

From this point of view, the Renaissance books of machines stand at the high-water mark of the old mechanics. Whatever could be done by ever more subtly deploying purely mechanical means of transmission, the Renaissance mechanicians suggested doing (and a good deal that could not). Tremendous expectations were aroused by their projects. When, as frequently happened, these expectations were disappointed, there might have been a reaction of general disillusionment, a feeling that men were condemned within certain limits and could not hope to break out beyond them. In fact, this did not happen. Individual inventors and projectors might have been cursed for failing to fulfil their promises, but generally there was a growing feeling that, if particular machines did not perform to expectation, others would, if only one could design them. As it became evident that the possibilities of the old mechanics were being exhausted, more imagina-tive minds turned to the creation of a new science, which could explain why machines that should have worked so well according to ancient theory either ran so slowly as hardly to be worth employing at all, or else, 'All would flie in sunder at the very first motion, and continually one thing or another out of order, and snap in sunder as soon as mended, because of the great strength is [*sic*] required to move the same.'[1]

These thoughts were certainly in the most imaginative mind of all those of his time, Galileo Galilei, when he set the scene of his dialogue *Two New Sciences* in the arsenal of Venice, the most advanced industrial complex of the age, and made his exposition derive from the problem 'Why the workers in the Arsenal employ stocks, scaffolding and bracing of larger dimensions for landing a big vessel, than they do for a small one'; which the workers explained by the supposed fact that a larger ship might collapse under its own vast mass, where a smaller one would not. Others saw the problem differently. If mechanical advantage in the transmission of power has its limitations, why not take the problem a stage further back, to the motor? This was the path that proved so fruitful in the long run. The real Industrial Revolution was a Power Revolution. It was the steam-engine, electricity, the internal combustion engine, which rendered practical the dreams of the past. Where the Middle Ages were able to replace the power of human or animal muscles by wind and water, the forces which Nature had set under their hands for the using, the Renaissance was able to squeeze the last drop out of such natural and easily available motors. The next stage, the search for a new artificial motor, was to prove much harder. Only one man in the sixteenth century, a Genevan lawyer called Michel Varro, appears to have seen this necessity clearly. In 1584 he suggested that the explosive power of gunpowder be used – an obvious suggestion as it now seems, and one which was taken up by several researchers a hundred years later. We find draughts of hot air being used as a motor in a few specialized cases, and even jets of steam applied to expelling fumes or intensifying the heat of a fire or a furnace, but these ideas remained marginal throughout our period. Only when all the possibilities of the old mechanics had been tried out could inventive ingenuity apply itself to the next problem.

[1] From Walter Blyth's *English Improver Improved*, published during the English Civil War.

THE AUTHORS

Jacques Besson was the first, so far as we know, to succeed in publishing his mechanical inventions to the world. When naturalized as a citizen of Geneva, in 1561, he described himself as 'of Colombières, near Briançon' in the Dauphiné, high up in the Alps on the south-eastern border of France, but nothing else is known of his origin and early upbringing. It may be only a coincidence that Oronce Finé, the greatest mathematician in France when Besson was a young man, was also a Briançonnais. Besson tells us that his own teacher was Pierre de Montdoré, known for a translation of the twelfth book of Euclid's *Elements*, and that he himself was already teaching mathematics at Paris in the early 1550's, but the first confirmatory note we have of his activities comes in 1557, when the City Council of Lausanne made a payment of two crowns to 'Jacques Besson the engineer, both for the water-engine delivered to their lordships, and as a first instalment for the designing of fountains'. The records are silent on the fate of Besson's fountains, but he turns up again two years later in Geneva, where he was granted right of residence in 1559, and citizenship free of charge in March 1561 for services rendered in teaching the art and science of mathematics. While in Switzerland he published his first book, a chemical work on practical distilling, with a preface recommending him to the public by Conrad Gesner, dispenser-general of useful knowledge to the whole of Protestant Europe. It would seem that he was not satisfied with the citizenship of Geneva, for we soon find him back in France, at Rouen in 1563, at Paris in 1565, at Orléans in 1567, teaching mathematics and demonstrating his wonderful inventions to an admiring audience. When his mathematical instrument, the cosmolabe, was pirated in 1567, he rushed back to Paris and published his own version, dedicated to Queen Catherine de Medici. In it he speaks of several of his other inventions; including the apparatus for raising sunken wrecks, and a sort of crude microscope, which was to be published in his great work. Even in Gesner's preface to his book of 1559, he had been portrayed as pre-eminently a deviser of wonderful machines, and he now began to seek an opportunity of showing them to a wider public.

In June 1569 King Charles IX came to Orléans. The city had become the storm-centre of that furious conflict between Protestant and Catholic which had been building up for the previous decade. During the 1560's Orléans had in fact changed hands more than once, now dominated by the Protestants, now by the Catholics, and the king's arrival was the signal for a pogrom of the Protestant faction. Besson was probably a Protestant himself, or so it would seem from his prolonged stay in Switzerland at Zurich and Geneva, the two capitals of militant Protestantism. He certainly had more Protestant contacts than was healthy – Montdoré his teacher, Eloy Gibert his printer, and Androuet du Cerceau, who engraved the plates for his book of machines. Fortunately he had friends in the right places, especially among those moderate noblemen who felt that loyalty to the State transcended religious differences. He presented himself before Charles and followed him back to Paris, as 'master of the King's engines'. Whether this involved more than the production of a great many designs for engines which were never tried out or put into practice we do not know. However, he must somehow have persuaded Charles to give him the money to publish his book of machines, which appeared probably in 1571-2 and which was dedicated to the king. It must have been done in a great hurry, for there is no proper description of the machines, only a Latin caption above each one and a French list of contents at the beginning; even the name of the printer is omitted. The reason can perhaps be guessed. The political situation had not been getting any better: in 1572 it broke, in the Massacre of St Bartholomew. Besson managed somehow to survive, but France had become too dangerous for Protestants, even with royal patronage. Geneva was impossible for some reason. Perhaps he thought that, having turned his back on Genevan citizenship to seek his fortune at the very Court of the Scarlet Woman, he would no longer be welcome there. At all events, he turned instead to London, and died there in 1573, unknown to the world.

The same year, 1572, that saw the Protestant Besson fleeing for his life to England, found the Catholic Agostino Ramelli on the other side of the fence, besieging the Protestants of La Rochelle. Little is known of his early life, except that he came from Ponte Tresa, a little town on Lake Lugano, on the border between Switzerland and the Duchy of Milan, and that he was born in 1531; but he seems to have followed a military career from an early age. His activity as a professional soldier took him to France, where he served under Henri, Duke of Anjou, soon to be king, as Henri III. Here Ramelli made his one and only appearance on the stage of history, for he was a member of a small party which set out in a boat to survey the fortifications of La Rochelle from the seaward side and plumb the depth of the harbour. A storm sprang up, Ramelli and his colleagues were captured and spent the next few months in a Protestant dungeon. Henri evidently rewarded him with the royal patronage, for on the frontispiece of his *Diverse et Artificiose Machine* he styles himself 'engineer of the most Christian King of France'. Nothing else is known of his career during the fifteen years between La Rochelle and the publication of his book in 1588, apart from a manuscript in which he explains the working of *his* patent mathematical instrument. His military bias is apparent from the large number of war-machines described – about a third of the book; Besson's book contained none intended specifically for war. Hydraulic engines occupy the largest part of both books, Ramelli playing every conceivable variation on this theme. He hints in one place that he had himself designed water-raising machines for a French nobleman, but we do not have the definite evidence we have in Besson's case that he actually installed a pump on a particular occasion. If he seems at times to lack Besson's imagination, Ramelli is remarkable for the comprehensive treatment of his subject. After he had finished, there was hardly a pump left to be designed on the traditional principles – workable or unworkable.

Whether or not he followed Henri III when he was driven from his capital on the Day of the Barricades later in 1588, Ramelli presumably chose the extreme Catholic party after Henri was assassinated, for he appears in a list of the prominent officers of the Catholic Leaguers during the siege of Paris as 'Agostino of Lugano, an old engineer'. However, when the siege was over and the League had collapsed, he must have made his peace with the new king, Henri IV, for we hear of him again, for the last time, in a document of 1604 as 'grand architect of the king'.

The third of our authors, Vittorio Zonca, is even more of a mystery than the first two. We do know that he died in 1603. His book was published posthumously by the Paduan printer Francesco Bertelli in 1607. Bertelli speaks of the book having 'come into my hands', but of its author he tells us nothing. All we know of him is what we are told on the frontispiece, that Signor Vittorio Zonca was 'architect to the Magnificent Community of Padua'. Our ignorance is particularly annoying in view of the fact that Zonca's book is in many ways the most interesting of all, for it is the closest to the actual mechanical practice of the time. He tells us in several places that a certain machine is being used at Padua or Venice, and suggests ways in which it could be improved. His range, which includes a number of textile machines, is much wider, and we can feel in him the sense of a technology on the move, when he speaks of the advantages brought by some actual innovation. Even so, his sober character was touched by the same dreams as his predecessors, for the book ends with a perpetual-motion machine as fantastic as any.

These, the most important machine-books, were written by professionals. A striking aspect of the story is the growing interest in machinery by amateurs. A number of our drawings have been taken from the books published by Faustus Verantius in 1616, and by Octavius de Strada in 1618. Verantius, born on the Dalmatian coast in 1551, spent his life as an administrator, secular and ecclesiastical. He became Bishop of Czanad in Hungary, although indeed this seems to have been primarily a reward for services rendered as Secretary for Hungary to the Habsburg Emperor Rudolf II; he never visited his diocese. His real interest in machines dates only from his retirement in 1608, when he entered the Barnabite Order in order to spend his last years in their monastery at Rome. So far from withdrawing altogether from the world, he speaks of his contacts with the engineer Targone and other friends who gave him suggestions for new inventions. Mazenta, the first biographer of Leonardo de Vinci, was also a member of the Barnabite house at Rome. Could Verantius have seen those celebrated manuscripts, now so famous, but then almost unknown?

A couple of years afterwards, Octavius de Strada published a collection of machines, purporting to be the designs of his grandfather Jacobus de Strada, Keeper of Antiquities to that same Habsburg Emperor Rudolf II. Jacobus had died in 1588, but there is no record of his ever having designed any machines. Having begun life as a goldsmith, he developed into a merchant of art and antiques the first man to make a business collecting paintings, sculpture and ancient coins for wealthy patrons on a European scale. For this, and for his published collections of ancient coins used as archaeological evidence, he has his niche in the Hall of Fame. Precisely because we are reasonably well informed about his career, it is rather odd to find him as a mechanician after his death, there being no trace of any mechanical interest during his lifetime. Perhaps it was Jacobus's son, Octavius senior, who made the collection, for he tried to sell a 'book of water-works', also described as 'various inventions of all sorts of mills and water-works', to the city of Nuremberg in 1593. The City Council, after referring the matter to their Master of Ordnance, turned him down on the grounds that some of the machines already existed, while others were so complex as not to be serviceable for their city. This might well describe the contents of the book published after his father's death by Octavius junior: some of the drawings are taken from Agricola's book of metallurgy, and others are far too involved to be of any real use.

In fact, decay set in after the publication of Zonca's book. We find machines getting ever more complicated, but the complications do not conceal the fact that the authors were just ringing the changes on a few over-worked themes, on which every useful idea had already been suggested. Ingenuity for its own sake suffered from a rapid diminishing of returns. Amateur dabblers tried to create a new theory of mechanics, illustrated by various subtle and ingenious – and unworkable – inventions. The book of Giovanni Branca, published at Rome in 1629, is of interest in this connexion. A few of his drawings are valuable, but most show evidence of the deterioration. Nobody was to match even the draughtsmanship of Zonca and Ramelli for the next half-century, not to speak of their imaginative powers. The machine-book was fleeing the centres of intellectual life, such as Paris and the Venetian Republic, for country towns; and, as the century drew on, the ideas become more and more fantastic, the provincial presses and universities taking a larger share in the production of works on the wonders of technology, and perpetual motion coming to dominate the imaginations of mechanical authors.

However, there is an aspect of the current amateur interest besides this fanciful toying with wild ideas. There developed a growing and intelligent interest in the achievements of mechanical invention on the part of an educated public curious about the way the world was moving. Travellers began to describe notable machines they had seen on their journeys, and so the more impressive feats of mechanical technology found their way into the guide-books, to be counted among the sights to see in famous cities. At first, attention was drawn to the more obvious examples of ingenious artifice, like the great clock of Strasbourg Cathedral (there is a fine working model to be seen in the British Museum), or the water-powered statues in the gardens of Pratolino, outside Florence. A man of real intuition saw further. The travel journal of Michel de Montaigne re-creates for us more vividly and succinctly than any ordinary traveller could, what it was like for a man of his sensitivity and intelligence to live in 1581, and more can be learned about the advance of mechanization from his description than from much longer accounts which merely repeat conventional observations. His acute interest in everything about him enables us to see pumping stations and smoke-jacks, not as the projects of imaginative engineers, but as they really were.

Not everyone can be Montaigne, but even blunter wits were now beginning to react in the same way. They discovered that machines need no longer be a subject fit only for artisans; gentlemen, too, could take pleasure in their ingenuity and even in their capacity for production. Indeed, a world was emerging which would be impressed by capacity for its own sake. Perhaps the Gargantuan visions of Rabelais inspired an urge to realize the grandiose in the everyday: the outsize cheeses of Count Somaglia pale beside the Great Bed of Ware or the Great Tun of Heidelberg, the biggest wine-barrel in the world, both of them products of the 1590's. It is this ambitious spirit, touched with the heroic at its best, though unfortunately often just bombastic, which informed our mechanicians. It appears in their delight in the ingenuity and vast capacity of their machines, and in an increasing readiness to apply the concepts of their philosophy to the tasks of the workaday world. Their wilder notions often seem to us ridiculous; sometimes they seem to be wasting their time on trivialities. It is always easy to poke fun at the errors of the past, but perhaps we can also feel some sympathy for these men, whose very names are now almost forgotten, for it is they who took the first faltering steps towards our mechanized world. If occasionally, like children taking their first steps, they seem to stumble, no doubt they can be forgiven. For it is largely under their inspiration that science and technology were wedded together in 'that marriage out of which', says Francis Bacon, 'there may spring helps to man, and a line and race of inventions that may in some degree subdue and overcome the necessities and miseries of humanity'.

A THEATRE OF MACHINES

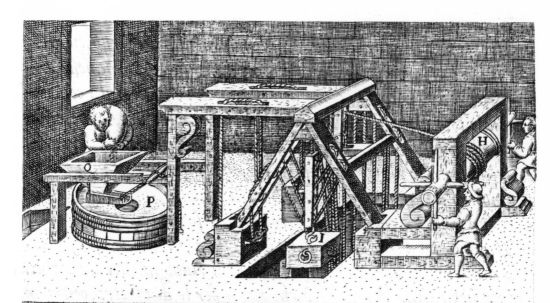

(*Ramelli*, Le Diverse et Artificiose Machine, *pl. 131*)

'In the year 1341 two novelties were started in the city of Milan by the lords of the city. The first is, that they devised how to make mills which are turned not by water or wind, but by weights and counter-weights, just as clocks are made. And there are many wheels there, and most subtle devices, and there is no need of any but one boy only, and they will mill 4 modici (about 70 bushels) of fine corn without stopping – an excellent milling indeed. Never was such work devised in Italy, although many have tried hard. . . .'

(GUALVANEUS DE LA FLAMMA, *Chronicle of the Deeds of the Visconti, Lords of Milan*, 1328–42)

WE SHOULD START WITH THE INVENTION, ABOUT 1300, OF A REASONABLY EFFICIENT mechanical clock, the great invention which opened the Renaissance. No less important than its value as a timekeeper was the inspiration it gave to ingenious minds to inquire whether the same principles could not be applied to different fields.

The same generation that saw the spread across Europe of weight-driven mechanical clocks also saw the 'clockwork mill'. Since the mill had to be 'wound up' fairly frequently it could hardly be called efficient; indeed, its motive power was human muscle, the most primitive and least efficient motor of all, and certainly more expensive than wind and water. But efficiency was not the only consideration. The excitement generated by a machine which ran of itself with one small boy to tend it can hardly be appreciated today. The automatic machine then seemed to have more than a little of the miraculous about it; a perpetual motion might be just around the corner. If mills of this kind were not too popular with the millers, they were certainly popular with the engineers. Apart from two drawings by Ramelli, there are several more in Strada's *Kunstliche Abriss*.

The drawing perhaps makes the mill seem rather more complicated than it really was, since the driving weight *I* appears twice, at the top of its motion and at the bottom, so that, as Ramelli explains, you can see what it looks like when the windlass has raised it, and also 'when it has completed its labour'. As it falls, it must raise the smaller weight at the back, which serves to slow down the motions of the mill. The rope which passes between the two weights is wound round the drum *K*, and so revolves it; the power is then transferred quite simply through a spur-wheel and pinion, crown-wheel and pinion combination to the axle-tree of the mill. The pinion, like most of those in the machine-books, is of the lantern type, two disks joined by a cage of bars.

13

(*Strada*, Kunstliche Abriss, aller handt Wasserkunsten, *pl. 100*)

'*I prayse the man, that did first Paper make,*
The onely thing that sets all vertues forth:
It shoes new bookes, and keeps old workes awake,
Much more of price than all this world is worth;
. . . The hammers thump, and make as lowde a noyse,
as Fuller doth, that beates his woolen cloth,
In open showe, the sundry secret toyes,
Make rotten ragges, to yeelde a thickened froth:
Then is it stampt, and washt as white as snowe,
Then flonge on frame and hang'd to dry, I trow.'
(THOMAS CHURCHYARD, *A Discription and*
Playne discourse of paper, 1588)

IF THERE IS ONE PILLAR ON WHICH THE WHOLE OF INDUSTRIAL PROGRESS RESTED IN the Middle Ages, it is surely the humble camshaft. A simple device involving no theoretical advance and adopted without excitement, it revolutionized a great number of trades. Exactly how, when, and where this vital tool was first employed remains a mystery. What we do know is that water-powered camshafts were used in the first of the European paper-mills to be founded – about 1150, at Jativa in what was then Moslem Spain.

If the Arabs first applied the camshaft to the manufacture of this new product, they failed to see what else could be done with it. In Western Europe, however, it was soon turned to a multiplicity of uses. If, as we have in the illustration, the cam lifts the head of a heavy hammer by raising the hammer's projected haft and letting it fall back in a short drop, a row of hammers can pound rags in water for paper. A longer drop on a narrower point can be obtained: if the cams on the shaft raise pistons held in a frame by their own projecting cams, the pistons will fall more sharply and can be used, as they were used, for grinding dyes; and, later, in the German mines, for crushing ores. When gunpowder came into use, every arsenal had its powder-mill, in which camshaft and pistons ground charcoal. The blacksmith, too, was able to work his bellows by a trip-hammer raised by a cam attached to the other end of the haft.

The text of Strada's book describes the illustration quite curtly:

'*In this picture it is clearly sufficient to see (and without need of initials to mark the parts) how the waterwheel turns its Axle with its Lobes or Arms attached, so as to raise and let fall back the six Hammers or Stamps which pound Rags small and wet in the two troughs standing before them. The Vat is also represented nearby with a grill-shaped Mould, then it must be taken by the Paper makers, and next you see the Press, under which the Paper already made is pressed with Felt lying in between: it is unnecessary to write any further explanation after that.'*

(*Strada, pl. 76*)

IF THE POSSIBILITIES OF THE CAMSHAFT BEGAN TO BE REALIZED AS SOON AS EUROpean industry started up again on a large scale after the retreat of the Dark Ages, the same can hardly be said for its sister, the crankshaft. The origins of the crank are hidden in the usual obscurity, but it is already represented in the form of a crank-handle in the eighth century. However, the crank-handle can hardly be said to have caught on during the Middle Ages. For the next five centuries it occurs only occasionally as the handle of a lathe or an organ, and only much later is the movement reversed and muscle-power applied to the central section of a crank to turn a drill. Finally, we find the human arm replaced by a connecting rod, and the crankshaft is born. The power can now be applied at the ends to achieve a reciprocal motion, or in the middle to obtain a rotary one. It soon became clear that the crankshaft would drive two rods as well as one, provided the power and the shaft were strong enough, and the fertile imagination of our sixteenth-century mechanicians readily made that up to four. Whether this was tried in practice, or very successful if it was tried, we do not know. Certainly those writers who kept closer to established practice, like Zonca or Agricola, show only crankshafts with single or double throw.

Part of the trouble lay, no doubt, in confused conception of the function of a crankshaft. Beroalde, in his commentary on Besson's book, wrote: 'as to the handle, one end does not continue in the same line as the other end, but is placed higher up, with regard to the axle which passes through the centre of the imaginary circle which is described by the revolution of the said crank-handle' – to which a later editor added 'as everyone who has a slight knowledge of Mathematics, will see well enough'. Well enough, perhaps, but vagueness of this sort might help to account for those curved crank-handles which were so common then, and long remained so, as if the maker wished to give an additional circular motion to his tool. So it was with Strada and his weird 'double cranks': if there was some value in this crooked shaft, reasoned the mechanics of the time, could not that value be doubled by doubling the crank?

(Ramelli, pl. 139)

A STRIKING EXAMPLE OF AN IDEA FULL OF POSSIBILITIES, WHICH YET REMAINED FOR centuries in suspension, is the endless chain. Chains of pots were already being used to irrigate the fields of ancient Egypt, and at least in Ptolemaic times they were being carried about the country on hire. By our period, this device had reached a high degree of sophistication, the original pots being replaced by square cases designed to raise the maximum of water in the minimum of space. Yet in all this time it seems never to have occurred to anyone that the same principle could also be used for the raising of solids. The first example we have of the endless chain, other than as a conveyor of water, is in 1561, significantly in a dredger used in the cleaning of a Dutch canal. If the chain could raise water from the canal, why not mud from its bed? Military engineers soon seized upon this useful notion. In the frantic rush of fortress-building which kept them so busy in the latter part of the sixteenth century, removing earth from moats and trenches for use in the erection of earthworks became a major problem. Another drawing by Ramelli shows a two-track ramp, up which cars of appropriate shape could be drawn by a horse-winch, the empty descending cars helping to raise the full ones by their weight. In books devoted specifically to fortification, like that of Lorini, we find similar ideas, such as aerial runways and cable-railways with cars shaped to fit the slope up which they had to ride. A real endless elevator only appears in one other place, a drawing by Besson, in which a chain of baskets filled with earth is drawn rather awkwardly up a ladder by crank and worm-gear at the top. Ramelli's idea, pictured here, seems neater. The boxes, shaped to fit the incline, and curved at the base so as to be able to slip over the drums marked *S* and *A* at each end of the chain, ride on double wheels, the chain running between the wheels. When the 'wheel made in the form of a cross', marked *S*, revolves, each arm of the cross engages with the rollers carrying box and chain alike. The weighted bar attached to the handle is intended as a sort of flywheel.

In spite of the uses to which the endless chain was being put at this time, it remained dormant for two more centuries. In fact, even in the construction of fortifications, it does not seem to have been frequently used, either because it was not very mobile, or else because unskilled labour was cheap enough to render it unnecessary. The countless applications of the conveyor-belt principle remained a potentiality.

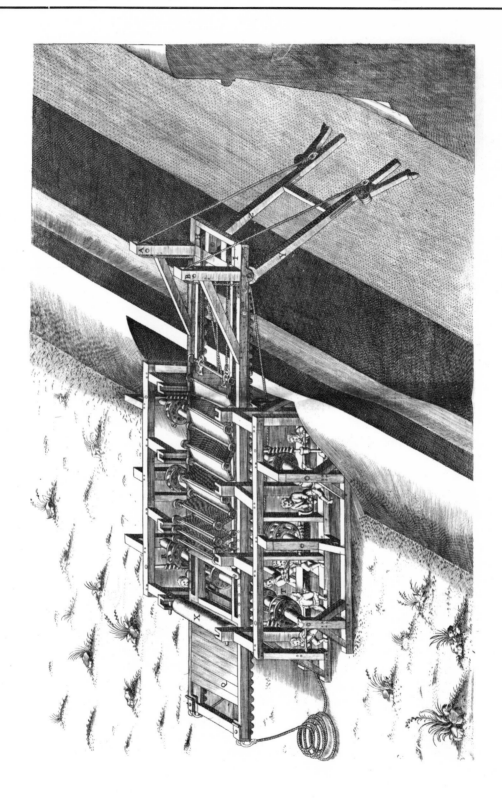

(*Ramelli, pl. 143*)

'These instruments are proved by plain experience to have inestimable force, from the many effects which are derived from them even in these times, when sometimes industrious Captains push or raise mobile bridges of immeasurable weight, over some stretch of water, or the height of a wall; or drive very large and heavy machines where it most pleases them, with inconceivable ease.'

(G. CEREDI, *Three Discourses on Raising Water*, 1561)

HAVING DEVISED INSTRUMENTS FOR DIGGING OUT THE MOAT, IT WAS OBVIOUSLY THE engineer's duty to think up ways of bridging it, particularly from the besieging side. The problem must have been attractive to Ramelli for, although collapsible bridges and scaling-ladders appear in many earlier and contemporary books on the art of war, nowhere do we find anything so elaborate as his invention. The sight of such a vast monster as his, relentlessly unfolding fresh extensions from its entrails, would surely intimidate the most tenacious enemy.

The frame of the bridge moves forward on what is essentially a rack-and-pinion. The four worm-gears $R\ S\ T\ V$, turned by capstan-bars, revolve four pinions set in their axles: one can be seen by the man's head at R. The pinions in turn push forward the toothed bar which runs underneath the whole length of the bridge. The roller X acts as a steadier; similar rollers can be placed further forward to enable the bridge to be pushed to the very edge of the scaffolding. When this is achieved, the two forked bars Y and Z are lowered by windlass (positioned under the bridge) and pulleys to provide a support. Now comes the *pièce de résistance*: 'for the enemy seeing only the frame of the bridge, cannot know what you mean to do, and if he should realize, he does not think you can do it so quickly'. The empty frame of the bridge is in position. The ropes attached to the front board of the flooring are pulled, and, suddenly, the hinged flooring boards shoot forward in the grooves at each side of the bridge to form a passage.

Ceredi's remarks suggest that bridges of this sort were sometimes actually tried out. However, references to their use are few. In the long run, problems of transport and the vulnerability of these contraptions must have persuaded most besieging generals to rely on bombardment – and starvation.

6. Expanding Bridge

(Ramelli, pl. 147)

CAESAR, AS HE TELLS US, 'THREW' A BRIDGE ACROSS THE RHINE. RAMELLI MUST HAVE taken him literally to have dreamed up the bridge portrayed opposite – which could be catapulted across the moat of a besieged fortress.

The lower half of the picture shows it being prepared for action. The bars A and B are held in twisted ropes which serve as the basic spring of the machine; the man on the left is giving a few extra twists. The bars are pulled down by winches, to which they are attached by a hook and ring; pawls and ratchets prevent the winches from slipping back. When the winches have done their work, the bars are fixed by a looped rope or bar to the roller G, which acts as an extra brake. The roller in turn is held fast by another looped bar, H, which fits over the peg provided. The machine is now ready to strike. The winch ropes are unhooked from the propelling bars; or, probably less effective and as Ramelli suggests in the upper picture, the pawls at E are simply raised; or both these things are done. When the word is given the looped lever at H is raised; immediately, the other looped bars pull the roller round, eventually releasing themselves. The big bars spring up, strike against the bar projecting from the bridge, 'lift it and all at once push up the bridge with great fury, throwing it across the moat'.

The bridge itself consists of the ten hinged sections 'in triangular form, but they have one angle cut off and extend very easily'. At the bottom, the sections are neatly rolled up like a mattress; 'in hexagonal form', adds Ramelli. At the top, they are extended, ready for the attacking force to trip gaily across, hopping from section to section, into the breach which their artillery has conveniently provided.

(Ramelli, pl. 46)

FEW MECHANICAL CONTRIVANCES MORE PLEASED AND FASCINATED THE RENAIS-
sance than the Archimedean screw. As a beautiful example of the simple, yet somewhat mysterious
mechanical principle of the screw, and as a novel form of water-raising engine, it combined the two main
strands in Renaissance engineering – the aesthetic, in the idea of the wonderful effects of mechanical motions
'to raise a great quantity with a little force' and the purely practical. An entire book was devoted to the
Archimedean screw – how to make it, how to move it, its advantages over all other hydraulic machines;
everything that might show its marvellous virtues and its reflection of Nature herself . . . 'for the spiral movement makes ascent easy to almost all things natural and artificial, from the sun in the heavens, to the vine,
ivy, gourd, and lupin twining round their supports'.

As its name suggests, this device goes back to the Hellenistic world, and perhaps even further back; there
is reason to believe that Archimedes, far from inventing it, found it already working in the fields of Egypt,
where it has remained in use ever since. But, whatever its origins, it certainly was not used during the
Middle Ages, and the story goes that a Milanese smith re-invented it for himself, 'before the books of Archimedes had been published', early in the sixteenth century. He is said to have gone wild with joy at his
discovery; his joy would perhaps have been modified if he had known that it was several times illustrated
in drawings of the previous century. About the same time, in the early sixteenth century, a tower of three
Archimedean screws was erected at Augsburg. It must have looked very much like Ramelli's drawing
opposite, except that the screws were directly above one another and driven off a central shaft, whereas here
they are extended in a row, so that each one can drive the next.

Let Galileo himself explain the working of the screw: 'We shall find that the water ascends in a screw
continually descending. . . . If we tilt the column of the screw through one-third of a right angle and a little
more, the course and motion through the channel will be depressed: therefore the water will move down
(from the point of entry to the first turn of the helix). And turning the screw round, its various parts succes-
sively displace one another and present themselves to the water in the same position (as that first part) whence
the water will go continually descending, and yet eventually will be found to have climbed from the bottom
to the top.'

(Ramelli, pl. 115)

'By Geometry, the waters, the Lowest stream in brooks and springs,
And the feeblest winds, will serve for millers,
And the grain, crushed between the rolling stones
Will pay his debt to his exacting mistress.'
(SALLUSTE DU BARTAS, *His Devine Weekes and Workes*,
translated by J. Sylvester, London, 1605–6)

THE WATERMILL WAS THE DEVICE WHICH CARRIED MECHANIZED ECONOMY TO THE
remotest villages of medieval Europe. It inspired the various applications of waterpower to other processes,
and made gearing and the simpler forms of power-transmission familiar to every builder and carpenter. The
archives of Renaissance monarchs and republics contain many projects for improved mills, which, by the
addition of a few extra wheels, would grind as much as two ordinary mills; even, according to some im-
modest claims, as much as four or eight mills. The waterwheel with horizontally set paddles was normally
less efficient than that with vertically set paddles; its advantages were that it could be encased in a narrower
basin, and that the head of water could be given more precise direction and greater force. In consequence,
it remained popular in many areas, particularly in the Alpine and Pyrenean valleys of southern France,
where carpenters continually experimented with the shape of their paddles in the effort to make use of every
drop of water.

Paddles shaped like half a spoon, like those shown opposite, are noted by Belidor, an eighteenth-century
hydraulic engineer, in a mill at Briançon, Besson's home town. In the latter years of the watermill they
became quite popular, and examples have been found as far north as Ulster. Their development was purely
empirical, a product of trial-and-error and intelligent craftsmanship. Nevertheless, the resemblance between
this form of paddle and the modern Pelton wheel is striking and cannot be accidental. Some other waterwheel designs distinctly recall the propeller-turbine.

27

9. Watermill (tubmill)

MOLETRINÆ AQVATILIS CONFICIENDÆ NOVA RATIO,
QVÆ VSIBVS MVLTORVM SATIS SIT FVTVRA,ET SI
MINVS AQVÆ SVPPETAT,QVAM QVOTIDIANIS MOLE
TRINIS SIT OPVS,MODO LABATVR AQVA E CLIVO
PAVLVM EDITIORE-

(*Besson*, Livre Premier des instruments mathématiques et mechaniques, *pl. 28*)

'The mill called the Basacle is one of the four wonders of Toulouse. . . . This mill was erected near the boat-station on the Garonne, with an entirely new device: there are fifteen watermills, following each other in order, enclosed in a single wooden building. The mill-stones, or dishes, are composed of pieces of stone ingeniously joined together, and bound round with iron clamps: each one is valued at some 1,000 gold pieces. The drum and great wheels are not turned round by the water of the river, but round basins have been built, like jars with wide mouths, into which an iron tongue descends vertically, which supports the mill. Vanes are fixed to its lowest part and are driven by the impulse of the water brought down upon them from above, through a channel. As they revolve, so the iron tongue on which the mill-stone rests, revolves too. Since this new work is unknown to the rest of France, it is worth seeing.'

(ABRAHAM GOELNITZ OF DANTZIG, *Ulysses Belgico-Gallicus*, 1631)

THIS IS ANOTHER STAGE ON THE ROAD FROM WATERWHEEL TO TURBINE. IT MAY WELL be that Besson's design was based on the wheel already existing at the famous mill of Basacle, which had been a tourist attraction even in the fifteenth century; but we cannot be sure exactly when this conical design was adopted. The commentator Beroalde remarks that 'this fashion is quite common, principally at Toulouse, and elsewhere at some villages where I have seen them'. However, he adds that 'our author has enriched it, in that the paddles of the wheel *vont en rond*' – he refers presumably to their helical pattern. It is clear from Besson's caption that he thought his device could save water, but not so clear how he arrived at this conclusion. Certainly, no one else concerned himself with precise calculations of water-flow and its control at this time, and there is no evidence that Besson did so. Perhaps he was inspired by his enthusiasm for the screw to try to adapt it to the waterwheel, although it must be said that this is the only conical screw in his collection.

(*Branca,* Le Machine, *pl. 19*)

IF WATER CAN BE RAISED BY APPLYING FORCE TO REVOLVE AN ARCHIMEDEAN SCREW, Branca must have reasoned, why not reverse the process? Let the water fall on the screw, which will then revolve and provide a new source of power. Or could he have been, in his invention depicted opposite, influenced by the helical vanes Besson used in his conical tubmill? Anyway, the plate shows an Archimedean screw in the sort of battery to which it was specially suited by its compact shape. In this case, 'the author has multiplied the machines in order to increase the force in the powers, so, the three motors being united together (which have, however, their origin in one only) the operation of turning the grindstone is carried out more easily'. Once again, we can see the germ of ideas, which were to prove so fruitful later on, rendered inefficient by the mechanical concepts of the time. The speed and power of the water are assumed to be constant throughout; but, Branca assumes the middle screw F will be revolved not only by the water falling into it from the trough L (with the same power as that falling on to the upper screw from the conduit A), but it will also be driven off the upper screw itself by the lantern and spur-wheel connecting them, and so, that much faster. It follows that the bottom screw will revolve with threefold power, being driven in effect by both the other two, and the little stream at the top will be magnified most wonderfully by the time it reaches the bottom. However, as Galileo pointed out, 'Whoever hopes by means of machines to gain the same effect without slowing down the movable body will surely be mistaken.'

Of course, it is easy to poke fun at these flights of fancy, and wonder what Branca had in mind for the framework at the top of the picture, or why he wanted such power for a simple mill. But we should remember that without these failures there could have been no Galileo. The early stages of an invention had to be based on trial-and-error, and it was the errors of the old mechanics that led to the creation of new mechanics seeking to correct.

(Branca, pl. 20)

BRANCA'S DESIGN HERE SHOWS A REVERSED ARCHIMEDEAN SCREW IN CLOSE-UP. THE more imaginative mechanicians were eager to display the versatility of their brain-children by showing as many applications as possible of the same *artificio*, which led to a certain repetitiveness in their books. It led also to the curious misconception of certain historians that Ramelli, Branca, and the rest failed to realize that a machine was an assembly of parts; apparently they are supposed to have imagined that each machine was a completely separate, *ad hoc* entity, a practical construction without a theoretical basis. The opposite is true. Branca's spinning-wheel shows clearly that he could, within his theoretical limits, tight as they were, create an *artificio*; it is when he comes to its application and when practical knowledge of other trades than his own is required of him that he is shaky. Apart from the question why so much power should be needed for a single spindle, he does not seem to have made up his mind whether he wants to spin woollen thread, as suggested by the distaff, or twist silk, as might be supposed from the curling wing *H* and the reel being carried upstairs for spinning. We are told that 'the lady holds the fork firm with her foot', but not why there has to be a fork at all.

Very few of the machines in our books belong specifically to the textile industry. Our engineers seem to have found few ways in which to apply their mechanical principles to spinning and weaving. Mechanization, however, continued slowly as the spinning-wheel spread across Europe, and there are references to improved looms – one inventor in Danzig created a loom for weaving 'four or five webs at a time without any human help'; but he was made away with for having endangered the livelihood of the poor weavers of his town. If there were improvements, they remained as a rule silent ones, operating under the surface of an industry apparently quite satisfied with its traditional ways, and when the mechanicians tried occasionally to see what they could do to speed the process up, they were apt to produce weird spinning-wheels like Branca's. Over his invention the poor spinsters of Danzig would certainly not have lost any sleep.

12. Calender

(*Zonca*, Nuovo Teatro di Machine et Edificii, *p. 56*)

'And so it is that now of late diverse Straungers by yonde the See have taken upon them to drie calendre Worsteddes with Gommes Oyles and presses . . . and if the same Worsted so dri-calendered taketh any Wete, incontinent it would skowe spotte and shew foule and ever continue still foule and woll not endure . . . whereas the said old Calendring of Worsteddes called wete calendring have been well used . . . in tymes past in the Citie of Norwich and yete is by persons havyng a conyng in the same.'

(*Statutes of the Realm*, 5 Henry VIII, c. 4, 1514)

OF ALL ASPECTS OF THE TEXTILE INDUSTRY, THE ART OF CALENDERING HAD MOST general appeal to our writers. Besson's only textile machine was a calender; Strada's book contains one and Zonca's two of them. Otherwise, this basic industry, which was to be the field for the crucial phase of the classical Industrial Revolution and which was then certainly the largest in Europe, both in terms of the employment it gave and the value of its products, was almost completely neglected. Only Zonca covers an at all wide variety of instruments, for, apart from a silk-spinning mill and two calenders, he also has a gig-mill – a frame with rollers for raising the nap on cloth with teasels – a fulling mill, a clothes-press, and a grinding mill for dyestuffs.

Although popular with the mechanicians, the calender does not play a particularly important part in the history of textiles. Like other innovations, it was not exactly welcomed to start with. The first certain information we have of it in England is Henry VIII's law forbidding any further improvements; just as the first we know of the gig-mill in England is the law that was passed against it. Makers of silk were probably the first to introduce calenders, for their industry was more open than others to new ideas: Besson writes that his calender will serve for 'waved silk or watered camlets', while Zonca writes 'with this machine smoothness and lustre is given to cloths, camlets . . . and the like'.

The calender was more obviously mechanized than other textile machines, and its interest to mechanicians lay in its profusion of levers, pulleys, and rocking beams. It gave them, too, a chance to play with reversing mechanisms: in the drawing opposite, the sledge carrying the pile of stones moves backwards and forwards while the horse has to keep walking in only one direction. Besson, to achieve a reverse mechanism, used a half-toothed crown-wheel, the toothed section engaging alternately with two pinions; Zonca, in his calender, adopts the more popular method of two crown-wheels engaging alternately with a single pinion – the pinion in the picture is being jerked from one crown-wheel to the other by means of the great lever *A*.

The cloths to be watered were wrapped round cylinders and placed underneath the sledge. Zonca has drawn two such prepared cylinders on the floor.

35

FILATOIO DA AQVA. I.

(Zonca, pp. 68, 74)

'We were also taken through the city (of Florence) to many houses where they make golden satin, cremoisy and other silken stuffs. We saw there a round wheel: a boy went into the centre and turned it round, working quite a hundred spindles at once, all of which were spinning silk. This same wheel also wound the spun silk as if on a reel.'

(*The Pilgrimage of Arnold von Harff*, 1497)

THE MULTIPLE SPINNING MILL, A MASTERPIECE OF MEDIEVAL MACHINERY, CER-
tainly deserves the enthusiasm lavished on it by Zonca, whose normally sober mind 'is dazzled within, at thinking how the mind of man could understand such variety of things, so many contrary motions moved by one single wheel'. So far as we know, the *filatoio* originated in the little Tuscan town of Lucca, where deeds of sale and hire from 1330 mention spinners with 240 spindles and list their many parts; these spinners, like the one at Florence described by Von Harff, were pushed round by hand. About this time, 1330, Lucca was torn by one of those ferocious and interminable feuds which seem to have been the main entertainment of medieval burghers, and many of her citizens fled, or were exiled, carrying their skills with them, to Florence, Venice, and Bologna. One of these refugees, settled in Bologna, had the ingenious idea of using waterpower to turn his mill; and this practice, once perfected, became standard and remained so until long after Zonca pictured it.

The first plate shows the driving mechanism. The waterwheel drives the 'garland' through three sets of

crown-wheels and pinions, the last being reversed. The 'garland' has two essential parts – the sloping 'serpents' *L*, carried by the cage of bars, and the projecting 'rubbers' *M*, held taut by counter-weights. Below the 'garland' can be seen enlargements of the gears, and a scale. The spinner itself, which encases the 'garland', is depicted in the second plate. The 'serpents' engage with the spokes of the gears *F*, which slowly revolve the reels of six hanks of silk to which they are attached. While the reels are turning, and so pulling up the silk, the 'rubbers' rotate the spindles which carry the silk below them; each strand of silk passes from the spool of the spindle, through a rotating S-shaped arm, through a little notched bridge at *O* and on to the reel. It is interesting to note that glass bearings were used in two parts of the machine. Leaving the notched bridge, the thread passes over a glass bar to keep it from catching on the wooden frame to which the bridge is secured; and the spindles revolve in 'little hats of glass . . . for if they were of iron and not glass, they would wear away the spindles which are pointed at the foot'.

39

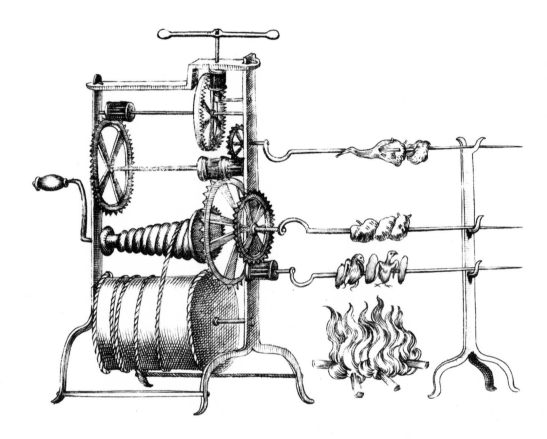

Molinello con tre spedi che si uolta dasse per forza de ruoute con il tempo a foggia di orologio come nella presente figura si dimostra

·19·

(*Scappi*, Opera, pl. 19)

'*At Brixen there is a fashion of turning the spit, which was by an engine with several wheels. A cord was forcibly wound round a large iron vessel: when it is released, its recoil is checked in such a way that this movement continues for almost an hour, and then you have to wind it up again. As to spits turning in the wind of the smoke, we had seen several of them. The people there have such great abundance of iron, that besides all the windows being latticed in various ways, their doors, their very shutters, are covered with strips of iron.*'

(MICHEL DE MONTAIGNE'S *Travel Journal*, 1580)

JUST AS THE EARLIEST MECHANICAL CLOCKS, WITH THEIR TRAIN OF GEARS DRIVEN by a falling weight, inspired attempts to invent clockwork mills, so later developments in the mechanism of the clock were followed in turn by their application to other purposes. The spring-and-fusee mechanism shown opposite was first employed in clocks about the middle of the fifteenth century. So it is curious that the first really clear representation of the whole mechanism did not come for more than a century with this spring-driven spit. Zonca's book contains a slightly later representation of the device, but his illustration has so much in common with the one here reproduced from the cookery book of Bartolomeo Scappi that one might suspect that he had based himself on Scappi, whose drawing is indeed much clearer, although it lacks Zonca's inset depiction of the spring-drum and the fusee itself.

When the spring replaced the falling weight as a motor, it was found necessary to counterbalance the slowing down of the mechanism in the last stages of its unwinding. The fusee, a 'screw pyramidal in shape', from which the driving cord was wound off, provided an answer. The cord ran off the narrow end first: as the fusee thickened, it exerted greater force on the two spur-wheels (which should be in the same axle) and so compensated for the weakening force of the spring. When a technique or machine is borrowed from one trade and applied to another, there are likely to be curious carry-overs, and it may take some time before it is realized that they are superfluous. In Scappi's spit, for example, the spits are curled into a shape imitating a crankshaft, perhaps with the intention of giving them more force, and the *tempo* at the top is borrowed from the escapement of a clock and serves to regulate the speed of its movement. Would it have been necessary to regulate the spits precisely, so long as they continued to revolve until the birds were done?

41

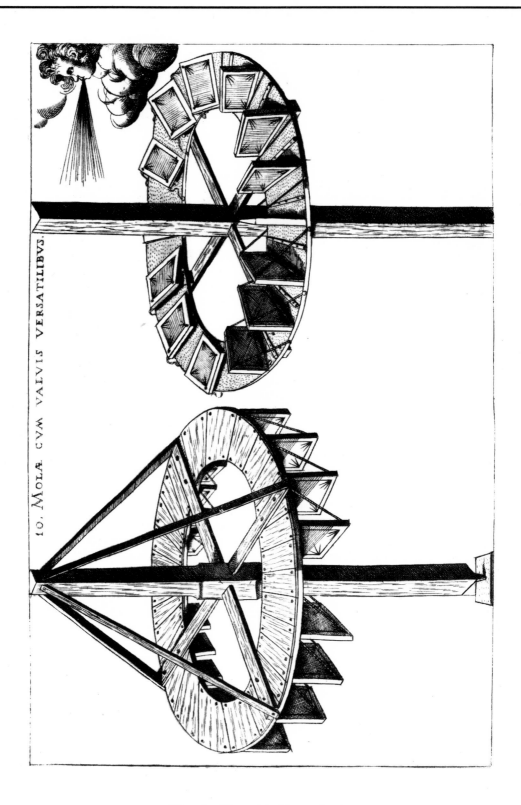

10. MOLÆ CVM VALVIS VERSATILIBVS.

(*Verantius*, Novae Machinae, *pl. 10*)

'Now, as the Winde huffing upon Hill
With roaring breathe against a readie Mill,
Whirles with a whiffe the sailes of swelling clout,
The sailes doo swing the winged shaft about,
The shaft the wheele, the wheele the trendle turnes,
And that the stone which grindes the flowerie corns.'
(SALLUSTE DU BARTAS, *The Devine Weekes*)

THE WINDMILL CREATED A GREATER IMPRESSION ON THE PUBLIC MIND THAN ANY other machine known to the Renaissance, and soon became part of the furniture of literature and folk-lore. For the first time an edifice, devoted solely to production and the satisfaction of humdrum physical needs, began to share the eminence of spires and towers; mills became a part of the landscape, surrounding the cities, like those on the ramparts of Bruges, so placed as to catch as much wind as possible.

The earliest European windmills appeared in the eleventh century. Their sails were always set more or less vertically and drove a horizontal axle parallel to the ground. Their use was hampered by the problem of keeping them facing the wind, into which they had to be turned as the wind changed direction.

Curiously enough, there were horizontal-sail windmills in Persia, with the sails fixed directly to the main shaft, earlier than any European windmills, but this idea was never taken up in the West until the generation before Verantius. Verantius claimed that the vertical sail was inconvenient, 'because having the Axle placed horizontally, which very often has to turn hither and thither, according to the change of Wind – therefore the whole mill has to turn and revolve very easily, and rest and be supported upon a single hinge. Then, in such Mills, the Grindstones are set in the upper part, i.e. in a place contrary to their nature.' To avoid this, he proposed six different types of windmill, with horizontal sails able to face the wind in any direction. His problem then was to direct the wind so that it would strike the sails on only one side of the shaft. The illustration opposite shows how he overcame this problem: when on one side of the shaft, the square sails, hinging freely, would be flattened by the wind and offer no obstruction; when on the other, they would be raised and held by ropes. The sails could be placed above or below the platform. The snag with all Verantius's proposals was the same: the area of sail actually exposed to the wind was always too small to give more than a minimal amount of power. Horizontal mills never caught on, and in the end it proved much easier to find a method of keeping the sails of an ordinary vertical mill facing into the wind.

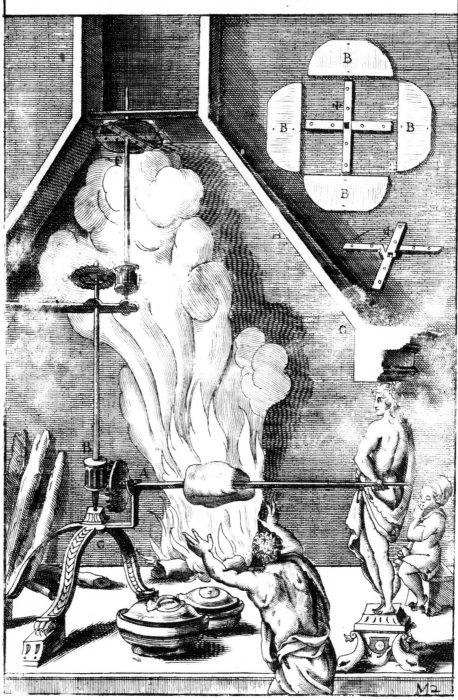

ALTRA MACHINA DA VOLTAR SPIEDI COL MOVIMENTO DEL FVMO.

(*Zonca, p. 91*)

'Since the Swiss are excellent workers in iron, almost all their spits are turned by springs, or by means of weights, like clocks, or else by certain broad light sails of pine that they place in the funnel of their chimneys, which turn with great speed in the draught caused by the smoke and the steam of the fire: and they turn the roast slowly – for they dry out the meat a little too much. These windmills are used only in the large inns where there is a big fire, as at Baden (on the road from Basel to Zurich). . . . They use almost the whole width of the kitchen for the chimney flue. This is a great opening, seven or eight paces square which narrows as it goes up to the top of the house. This gives them room to place in one spot their big sail, which with us would take up too much room.'

(MONTAIGNE'S *Travel Journal*)

ALTHOUGH HISTORIANS OF TECHNOLOGY HAVE SNIFFED AT ITS 'TRIVIALITY', THIS primitive 'rotissomat', turned by the draught of hot air rising in the chimney, was the first practical heat-engine – the first machine to be driven by an artificially produced power, rather than one provided by nature or human muscle. Wherever it was used, it abolished a disagreeable, boring, and unhealthy job – surely one of the main purposes of technological progress. It was, in fact, a watermill turned upside down, in which the fan-wheel revolved an axle through three sets of crown-wheels and pinions, a standard combination for transmission in medieval mills.

Zonca and Montaigne seem to have thought it was the smoke itself which did the work, and so did John Dee, an Elizabethan mathematician and propagandist of science, who spoke of 'Mills by Smoak moved'. The origins of this machine are unknown, although Leonardo da Vinci sketched a design for a simpler version. The kitchen of a large inn, where roasting would go on throughout the day, seems the most likely place, perhaps in Switzerland where Montaigne saw the machine he describes in his *Travel Journal*, where inns were busy, and where the example of waterpower was apparent on every side. At all events, these devices do not seem to have been common outside the Alpine region. Perhaps it was some unknown Swiss hotelier who first noticed that an artificial current of hot air had the same effect as a natural current of cold water. If so, all honour to him: he has his place with Watt and Papin among the fathers of the Power Revolution.

(*Branca, pl. 2*)

'This construction (named The Engine, because of its subtlety) is based on the doctrine of Aristotle, at the beginning of his Mechanical Questions, where he speaks of "Another circle which moves at the same time with opposed motions, for it moves simultaneously inwards and outwards." The water, then, moves a wheel: and this moves two more in opposite directions: between their axles passes the ingot, or strip of metal, until it is left in that thickness which the money requires: and finally between two dies of refined steel, on which the royal arms are engraved: and with a movement in opposite directions, as Aristotle teaches, the ingot emerges stamped on both sides. Then it is cut in a round lathe with male and female parts with much ease, and little labour; and so with the other instruments, forge-bellows, hammers, which are very big – and all moved by water-wheels.'

(DIEGO DE COLMENARES, *History of the Illustrious City of Segovia*, 1637)

THE OLD-FASHIONED HOUSEHOLD MANGLE SEEMS NOW ON THE POINT OF DISAPPEAR-ing completely into limbo; in its day, however, it was the key to many mechanical innovations of the Renaissance. The rolling mill for flattening out strips of metal makes its first appearance, like so much else, in the sketch-books of Leonardo da Vinci, and it spread gradually throughout the century after its introduction, remaining always something of a novelty. A recent historian, Henri Michel, has suggested that the rolling mill produced a revolution in the quality of those instruments which require an even surface, making it possible to obtain a thickness of plate and a texture of surface far more regular than could be achieved by the old method of hammering out.

An attempt was made to apply the principles of the rolling mill to the printing of coins or medals, the appropriate die being cut into the face of the rollers. This was first tried in Germany in 1550; but most of our information relates to a Spanish rolling mill. In 1583 the Archduke of Austria sent off an entire mint to his second cousin, Philip II of Spain, plant, workers, and all, which was set up with its 'New Engine' at Segovia. It caused quite a stir at the Spanish Court, and nearly a century later an English writer cited it as an example of mechanical automation.

The Segovian engine must have looked something like Branca's design. The important difference is the source of power. Branca has introduced something like the Baden smoke-jack, a hot-air machine, for 'the chimney is made in such a manner that, sending up the hot air of the fire and smoke, it turns the flyer *I*'. *I*, the peculiar object wound round the top of the chimney, is meant to be a wheel with vanes inside it. Branca must have appreciated that he would not get much power out of his draught of hot air to have piled on the gears the way he has, in an effort to increase the power.

TORCHIO PER STAMPAR I DISEGNI CON I RAMI INTAGLIATI.

(Zonca, p. 76)

IF THE CAMSHAFT WAS THE CRUCIAL DISCOVERY OF MEDIEVAL INDUSTRY, THE roller, especially in the form of a roller-press, proved hardly less fertile for the Renaissance. Apart from rolling and slitting metal plates and striking coins, it had many other uses. Opposite is an engraver's press, 'for printing drawings with engraved copper-plates', the printing surface being the copper-plate itself, resting between the board C and the backing-felt D. A rotary press was devised in Rome at about this time, but it came to nothing.

It would seem that the concept of the roller-press – that is, the mangle – went through various stages. In the oldest printed illustration each roller has its own separate crank, while in Branca's rolling and coining mill the two rollers are geared together. Where the pressure need not be very great, the simple mangle type works perfectly satisfactorily. In Zonca's machine, the lower roller is driven in the opposite direction to the upper one by the friction of the board rolling over it. Wooden bearing-blocks B are provided to hold the rollers firm, and facilitate their removal whenever necessary.

One striking feature of Zonca's description is his insistence on the right materials. Thus, the rollers should be of box-wood or pear. He adds some advice on the ink: 'Take the shells of nuts or bitter almonds, or lampblack, or the lees of wine or malmsey (this is most in use), grind it up with water first on a stone of best porphyry, then when it is ground, leave it to dry, then dissolve it in varnish – either coarse varnish or that of amber which is better – first warming the copper-plate before the ink is spread on it' (as the boy in the plate is doing, over the brazier with the dogs' heads). We are assured that 'if proper care is taken, there is no doubt that a thousand prints can be taken, and with a little touching up even two thousand off each plate'.

Was the roller-press for prints inspired by the rolling mill for plates, or might it have been the other way round? Engraving was at first only very rarely used for book illustrations. Henri Michel has ascribed the tremendous improvement in maps and mathematical instruments about the middle of the sixteenth century to the rolling mill. It seems reasonable to ascribe the improvement in illustration to the roller-press and copper-plate; for whatever the aesthetic merits of woodcut, copper-plate surely carries off the palm for the amount of detail it can bear. All our mechanicians proudly stress on title-page or preface: 'Illustrated on copper.'

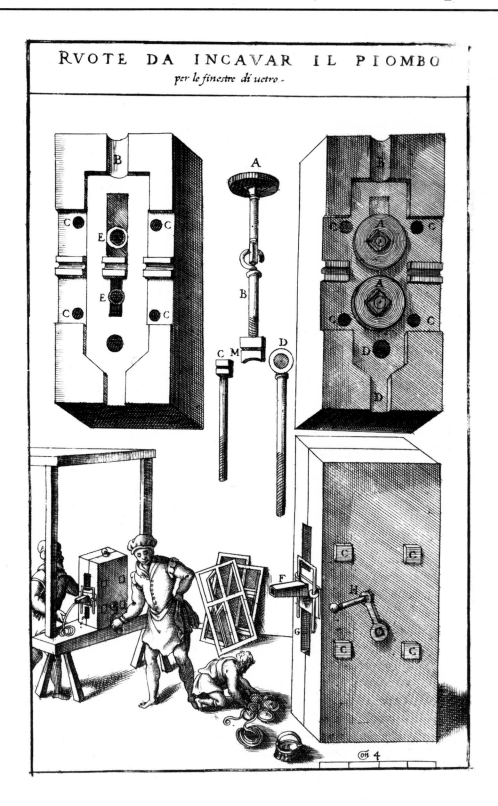

RVOTE DA INCAVAR IL PIOMBO
per le finestre di uetro.

(Zonca, p. 79)

THESE WHEELS FOR CUTTING LEAD FOR GLASS WINDOWS ARE REALLY ANOTHER
type of rolling and slitting mill, this time in miniature. 'Among many similar machines I have seen,' writes
Zonca, 'this one is one of the most beautiful and most ornate.' And functional. Large quantities of lead
strips must have been needed for the great stained-glass windows of medieval churches. The individual panes
of glass were cut extremely small, and the proportion of lead to glass was high. The lead strips originally
were cast, and doubtless trimmed, by hand; and it was only about forty years before Zonca's book appeared
that this useful handmill made its first appearance – in Jost Amman's collection of Woodcuts, 'Of all
Illiberal, Mechanical, and Sédentary Arts'. In Amman's book, the glazier is depicted with a little instrument
very similar to that illustrated by Zonca, except that it stands upon a tripod.

Although this is one of Zonca's most detailed and attractive drawings, the plate leaves certain points
obscure. Where, for instance, is the lead fed into the machine? What is the precise function of the groove
which in the left-hand picture crosses the instrument in three sections, yet in the right-hand picture is in
two sections only? However, the machine's general functions are quite clear. The wheels A are revolved by
means of handles, one on either side of the machine. The lead is drawn between these wheels, and forced
through the pipe leading to mouthpiece F. We are told that both the wheels and the mouthpiece actually cut
the lead, and should be made of good steel. The cuttings slip through the slots above and below the mouthpiece; some can just be seen dropping out of the machine when it is at work. The holes at C give the device
a complicated appearance; in fact, these four holes, with the four screws also marked C, merely fasten the
two parts together. D holds the instrument firm on its base. B with its projecting hook makes it portable,
while the tenon M on the bottom of the screw B presses down on the upper wheel. Zonca is usually careful
to be as clear and accurate as possible, but it seems that in this case he did not appreciate what was happening.
In fact he compares this relatively simple mechanism with that of clockwork . . . 'those little figures which
walk on a table or dance about, to the great astonishment of the spectators, the cause being hidden and only
the effects visible'. Of the structure and performance of his own machine he writes 'not knowing how the
parts within the machine work, those who look on are filled with wonder'.

51

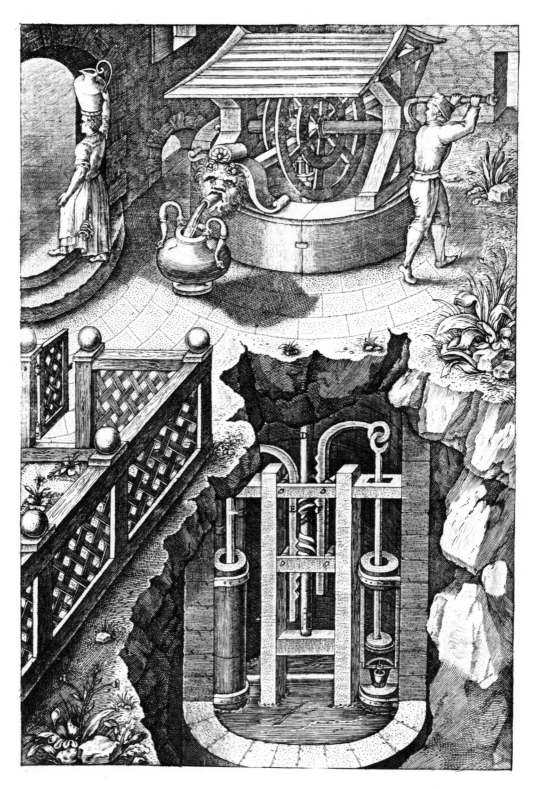

(*Ramelli, pl. 2*)

'There was in our inn at Augsburg an engine of pieces of iron, which fell to the bottom of a very deep well in two places, and then, up at the top, a boy worked an instrument, making these pieces of iron go up and down two or three feet; so they beat and press the water at the bottom of the well one after the other, and, pushing the water with their pumps, they force it to gush up through a lead pipe which carries it to the kitchens, and wherever there is need of it.'

(MONTAIGNE'S *Travel Journal*)

TIME-SAVING WAS OF GREAT IMPORTANCE IN THE GREAT INNS ON THE MAIN TRADE routes of Europe. Domestic staff also had to be kept to an economic minimum. The palaces of princes and nobles were not analogous, because even the richest of innkeepers could hardly afford the army of servants deemed necessary for maintaining a great lord and his household in style and comfort. And tasks which in private houses need a limited time each day sometimes had to be performed almost continuously in busy inns. It was here, therefore, that mechanization first began to relieve the physical strain of household work. Here, too, travellers from abroad had the opportunity for observing ingenious foreign devices.

This mechanism, set in a well in the courtyard of an inn, is fairly typical. It manages to be both ingenious and clumsy. Two upper wheels – a combination of flywheels on the outer circle, and crown-wheels on the inner – are equipped with teeth on half their circumference. These therefore engage alternately with the pinion C, causing the shaft D to revolve in alternate directions. The two worm-gears on the lower part of the shaft will then drive the toothed bars E and F up and down, and these in turn will raise and lower the pistons alternately. Roller bearings have been installed to prevent the pistons slipping. The pump on the right has been cut away so that it is possible to observe the action of the piston inside the cylinder, and the valve at the base.

(Ramelli, pl. 9)

'Thence to a gate of the town . . . where we observed that a large channel of water flows under the bridge we had passed over . . . and sets in motion a great number of wheels, which drive several pumps, and raise the water of a spring, which is in a very low place, through two lead conduits, to the top of a tower fifty feet high at the least. There it pours into a great stone vessel, and from this vessel descends through some more conduits, and thence it is distributed through the town, which is by this means alone quite peopled with fountains.'

(MONTAIGNE'S *Travel Journal*)

FROM THE EARLY SIXTEENTH CENTURY ONWARDS, WHEN THE GREAT EUROPEAN cities began to press more heavily on their water resources, more mention is made of large-scale pumping stations equipped with a whole battery of pumps. This development was brought about by more than the need for exploiting those sources of water which could not be brought to town centres by the force of gravity, as had been done in the aqueducts of antiquity. The demand for improved water supplies also arose from a desire for refinement which was expressing itself in other aspects of the life of that period. Watermen had adequately supplied London with water throughout the Middle Ages, but though these men protested, in the 1590's the City Fathers installed a pumping mechanism which would bring piped water direct from river to house. At least one nobleman living in the City felt it to be his feudal duty to continue to patronize 'his' waterman. The new system was hardly more sanitary, though it may have created that illusion.

German and Flemish cities were the first to install mechanical pumps on any considerable scale. The pumping stations of Augsburg were widely renowned. One of them raised water above first-floor level, as did the pumping system at Constance which was under construction at the time of Montaigne's visit.

The two pairs of pumps illustrated here work on the rack-and-pinion principle by means of pistons driven by four toothed bars and four pinions. So that the drive may be from the centre, and the pumps functioning alternately, a double reverse mechanism is installed at the centre. When put into operation this must have imposed a considerable strain on the teeth. But wooden teeth were inexpensive and easily replaced. Only half of each crown-wheel in the axle of the waterwheel is toothed. These therefore engage alternately with the pinion between them. This pinion drives the upper crown-wheel *E*, which then drives the two upper pinions in alternate directions.

55

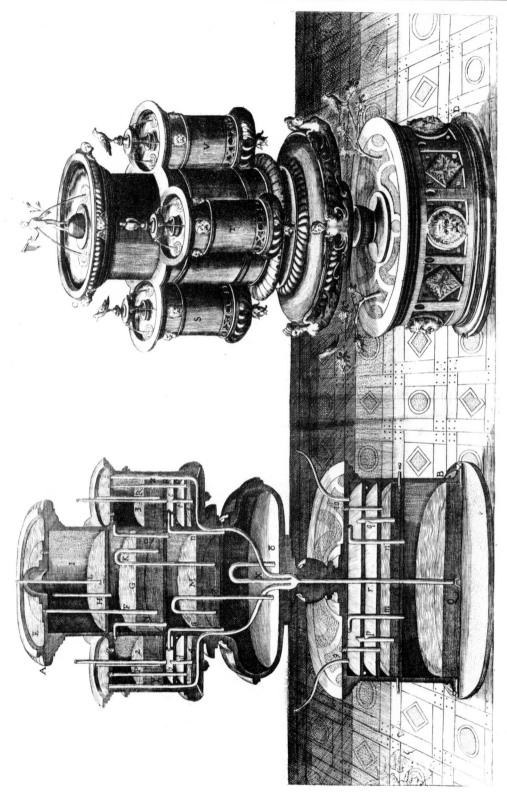

(*Ramelli, pl. 186*)

'These birdes by the mathematicall experimentes of long silver pipes secretlye inwinded in the intrailes of the bough whereon they sate, and undiscernablie convaid under their bellies into their small throats sloaping, they whistled and freely carold their natural fieldnotes. . . . But so closely were all these organising implements obscured . . . that everye man there present renounst conjectures of art, and sayd it was done by inchantment.'

(THOMAS NASHE, *The Unfortunate Traveller*)

THE IMAGINATION AND INGENUITY OF RENAISSANCE ENGINEERS WAS STIMULATED by the passion for complex and imposing fountains which obsessed the courts of Europe at that time. In Ramelli's day the craze had spread to the villas and mansions of country gentlemen. Basins merely overflowing with water were too dull. Jets of water might provide a background, especially if august owners with a well-developed sense of humour could direct concealed jets at their guests and courtiers when these were innocently admiring the fountain. Even so, the perfect water-garden and its statuary deserved more than jets, however divertingly placed. Birds must twitter, dragons must roar, Pans pursue nymphs, and giants raise their clubs. Only thus could a taste for machinery in the garden be satisfied.

A few sketches and enthusiastic descriptions survive of the automata which enthralled visitors to the Saint Germain of Henri IV and the Pratolino of Duke Francesco de' Medici. Therefore there is particular interest in this drawing of a fountain and the sketch in section which shows its working principles. The accompanying text describes in detail how the automata of the fountain are contrived so that the birds on the lower tier of basins and on the branches projecting from the base will sing and flutter.

'Wishing for a greater curiosity that the birds should move when they feign their songs, the bodies of the said birds are formed quite empty within; then the wings, tail and beak are made separately (that is, the lower part of the beak), and an effort should be made to have them conform to natural ones. Then the tail, wings & beak are attached in such fashion that they can move, when the air forced out through the pipes VT will play in their bodies: and this will easily be done by sticking the said parts with very fine leathers, in order that the air enclosed in the concavity of these birds, can not escape, unless impelled by force & so the air which is constrained within their bodies, will move at intervals through all their parts. Then the tails of the said birds are fixed into their rumps, in such a way that the part which enters into the body, may serve as a counterweight to the said tails, which must be set in balance, by means of an iron thread which runs through them from one side to the other. So the lower parts of the birds' beaks are fitted on, which, being impelled by the air which enters their bodies, will gently move & feign their songs as if they were alive, and last until compartment 8 shall be full of water.'

57

(Ramelli, pl. 100)

'At one place in the State of Lucca, I came across an instrument which is half derelict through the negligence of the Government: and this defect causes much damage to the country round about. This instrument was made for the task of draining the land in these marshes, and rendering it fertile. A great trench was dug: at the head of it three wheels, which were moved continually by means of a stream of running water, which fell from the mountains upon these wheels, with certain vessels attached to them drew the water from the trench on the one side and poured it out on the other into another, higher trench: which trench, made to this end, and protected by a wall on each side, carried this water into the sea. Thus the whole country round was drained.'

(MONTAIGNE'S *Travel Journal*)

HYDRAULIC ENGINEERING WAS NOT CONFINED TO DECORATIVE WORK. THIS WAS THE first Golden Age of marsh drainage in Italy and the Low Countries. What had started as small-scale improvements by private landowners now began to assume national dimensions. As the interest in land reclamation spread to centralized states such as France and England, kings and governments examined possibilities for draining the marshes in their sovereign states. In 1561 the Venetian Republic, always mercantile and progressive, created a special 'Commission for the Uncultivated Lands' charged with improving the whole Venetian mainland on the basis that it comprised one great estate with resources and production capable of unlimited expansion.

Medieval methods of drainage by ditching and diking proved inadequate for the grander schemes. The sumps created by major drainage works had to be emptied by machinery, in the form of waterwheels where streams were adjacent, by horsepower where these were non-existent. The vagueness of Montaigne's phrase 'certain vessels' (*certi vasi*) leaves it uncertain whether he means piston-pumps as illustrated here, or Archimedean screws such as appear in Ramelli's next drawing. A battery of pumps was common. In Montaigne's description there are three wheels, each driving its own 'vessel', while in Ramelli's drawing a single wheel drives a rocking beam by means of a crankshaft. It can thus drive four separate pumps, which force the water into chests G and H, from which it empties in this example into the stream which drives the wheel. The process of drainage is vividly presented by contrasting the drained land already planted as an orchard with the lower boggy area.

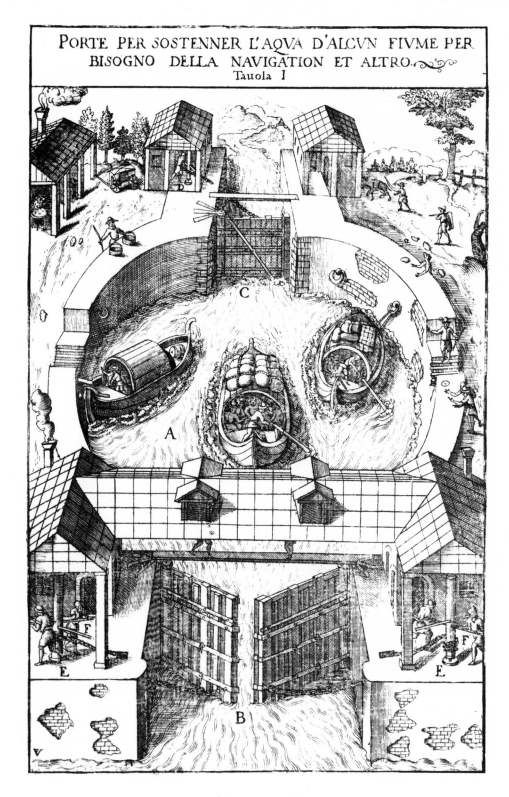

PORTE PER SOSTENNER L'AQVA D'ALCVN FIVME PER
BISOGNO DELLA NAVIGATION ET ALTRO.
Tauola I

(Zonca, pp. 9, 12)

'On both banks of the Brenta, there are many beautiful palaces and pleasure-gardens, and then the boat presents itself between Padua and Lucefusina at two stone locks, or great cisterns, built of stone, several feet high, and let down into a canal. The locks have an upper and lower gate, of such a size that a fairly large boat may go through; if the boat comes from Padua, the lower gate is shut, and the whole lock is allowed to run full of water, so as to be at the same height as the water of the Brenta. So when the boat has gone in, the upper gate is shut, and the water in the lock let run again, and the boat sinks down in the lock until it is at canal-level, then it travels on. But if the boat is going from Venice to Padua, the boat is allowed to enter (for the water in the lock is at the same level as the canal), then the gate is shut, and the lock let run full of water, so the water lifts up the boat, so that one can travel up the Brenta; which is therefore a beautiful invention, by which without any trouble the boat can be lifted up and down without unloading.'

(HANS GEORG ERNSTINGER'S *Travel-book*, 1593)

ONE ONLY OF LEONARDO'S NUMEROUS INVENTIONS SEEMS TO HAVE BEEN MADE KNOWN to the public; the rest disappeared into his notebooks. Pound locks, composed of a central basin and two gates which could be raised vertically by a winch, like a portcullis, were invented a century or more earlier. But the two devices shown here may be connected with a sketch of Leonardo's which described a lock known to have been installed at Milan in 1497. The first illustration shows the mitre gates *B*, the upper gates described by Zonca as 'a gate divided into two parts, so joined that they stand at an angle against the flow of the water, so as to break its impetus'. Other engineers had experimented with gates which would not have had to be raised to the full height of the lock. One of these designers, Alberti, suggested a gate which would revolve on a central axle, with the doubtfully successful result that though easily opened it would reduce the width of the channel by half. Leonardo's solution seems to have been in general use from about the middle of the sixteenth century. It is commemorated in a medallion issued in 1587 to celebrate the opening of the Brussels–Ruppel Canal in Belgium. In many instances, as here, the lower gate consisted of a single leaf, because this is the gate which had to withstand the least pressure. Yet because it would have had to open upstream in the same way as the upper gates, surely the chain and capstan *D* are misplaced? But perhaps this is deliberate, and intended to present a clearer view of the gate.

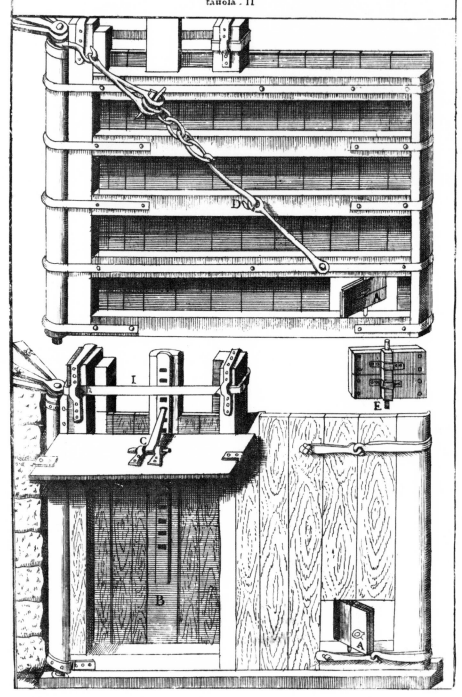

The second picture shows Leonardo's second device. His problem was to let the water in and out of the basin rapidly and without turbulence. Part of the gate *B*, in the lower half of the picture, was capable of being lifted in its groove by means of an iron lever. The bar and iron peg *C* served as a ratchet to hold the slide at the desired height, so that water could flow through. However, Zonca states that 'the use of this little gate is given over, because of its slowness, and the other sluice is becoming usual'. The 'other sluice' is the small swivelling door shown in the gate at *A* and independently at *E*. As in Leonardo's original drawing, it is opened by a chain.

Could Leonardo have adapted this idea from Alberti's swivelling gate? It is also possible, however, that the mitre gate, which proved invaluable to canal and river navigation, did not originate with Leonardo. Zonca states that the locks he describes are similar to those on the Brenta at Padua, Strá and Dolo. It is known that the famous locks at Strá were erected in 1481 by two brothers from Viterbo. The *ingegno* which they undertook to install might be the pound lock itself, with its upper and lower gates, though it could conceivably have referred to mitre gates or a simple sluice. However, though the earliest drawing of the locks at Strá, dated *c.* 1538, shows no mitre gate, the matter remains unsolved.

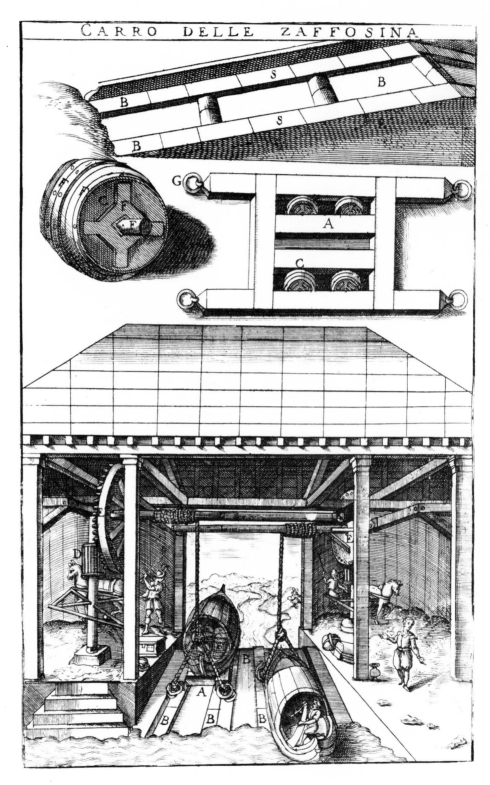

CARRO DELLE ZAFFOSINA

(*Zonca, p. 58*)

'On this stream are many houses and villages, such as Strá, Dolo and Lucefusina, where the said river flows into the Adriatic: but one can not likewise pass through in a boat, for a strong weir of wood at that point prevents the canal (which is several feet higher than the sea) from running into the sea: over this weir, the boat passes on a great sledge with rollers, made for this purpose, through an ingenious traction with horses, as far as the sea.'

(ERNSTINGER'S *Travel-book*)

THE SLIPWAY AT FUSINA WAS EVEN MORE FAMOUS THAN THE LOCKS OF STRÁ. IT IS mentioned in every contemporary travel-book as the place on the way to Venice where travellers were compelled to halt for a meal while their boats were hauled into the lagoon. Draw-overs of a rudimentary kind existed in the Middle Ages, and sometimes appear in early town maps as space-fillers outside the town, in company with windmills, cranes, gallows, and similar amenities. These early slipways consisted usually of a pair of winches, with perhaps a few rollers in the track to ease the passage of a boat. The interesting innovation here, as Zonca points out, is the carriage. This could be the first step towards the invention of railways.

The four rollers (*C* in the upper picture), 'made of nut-wood or oak, and bound and mounted in iron', exactly fit the passage *A* between curbs *B*, so that the carriage slides along the curbs. Other rollers appear to have been provided in the slipway, which was 'made in the fashion of a roof with a very obtuse angle'. The boat is then drawn up until its keel rests in the groove in the centre of the sledge, between *A* and *C* in the upper picture. It can then be hauled up and over the incline without danger of itself or the carriage slipping.

In fact, an earlier drawing shows that there was no more than one track, with both horse-winches on one side of the slipway. It is Zonca's suggestion that it would be better to place them on either side, as in his illustration. In this way two boats could use the slipway at the same time, and be hauled in opposite directions without interfering with each other.

(Ramelli, pl. 176)

'Thereby a Crane shall stead in building, more
Than hundred busy Porters did before.'
(SALLUSTE DU BARTAS, *The Devine Weekes*)

CONSIDERING THAT MECHANICS WERE DEFINED AS 'THE RAISING OF HEAVY WEIGHTS by a small power in such a way as to deceive nature', it is not surprising that early writers on this subject devoted a great deal of space to hoists, 'cranes, gybbettes, and engines to lift up or force any thing'. Here mechanical principles are seen at their most basic. But the quickness of the designer's hand deceives the eye of the innocent beholder, and there is an illusion that the devices are complicated and mysterious. The wheels and pulleys, the curling volutes and grimacing carvings (including the figurehead who shields his ears with his hands) sustain that impression. But the machine is no more complicated than the ordinary hand cranes which are used in modern goods yards. It consists simply of a pinion, spur-gear and worm-gear, engaging with the drum of a windlass which is divided in halves so that two ropes can share the strain.

The interest of the drawing lies in the base of the crane, which revolves on a turntable. This is the first known illustration of this simple but important device. The big wheel P carries the superstructure of the crane and revolves between roller bearings X, as in a modern crane. Cranes which slew and swivel frequently appear in the writings of the Middle Ages. And early windmills were capable of being levered round to face the wind. But in such cases the whole superstructure depended upon a single pivot. This is a far clumsier and less secure method than the turntable. It is in fact another example of a device traditionally used for one purpose being ingeniously adapted for another. Rollers were always used for pulling a heavy object from one place to another. Could they not therefore be used for pulling an object around in a circle? Or, better still, could not the object be placed between two rollers, so as to complete the operation faster and with greater ease?

(Ramelli, pl. 189)

'You have a storehouse of machines of war and machines to move weights, your Excellency having manufactured perhaps twelve of different types, some to draw along the ground, others to lift up immeasurable weights with very little force; such as one, which has one single toothed wheel, and at need draws five of our cannon, moved by the strength of Gradasso, your dwarf; and another which, with only one ounce of force placed on the handle which turns it, gives motion to fourteen thousand pounds weight. . . . These machines can be carried by a mule, and some of them even by a man, and are used for various purposes . . . but especially to handle and transport great pieces of artillery. Certainly, if in the year 1529 the French captain Count de Saint Paul had had one of these instruments in his retreat into Piedmont, he would not have lost a cannon in the mud when a bridge broke under it: so much time was wasted trying to get it out that Antonio da Leyva attacked him and captured Captain, cannon, and all. . . .'

(FILIPPO PIGAFETTA dedicates his *Mechaniche* to Giulio Savorgnan, Superintendent-General of the Artillery and Fortifications of the Venetian Republic, 28 June 1581.)

THE DEVELOPMENT OF ARTILLERY CREATED A NEW SERIES OF PROBLEMS FOR THOSE people responsible for moving large and unwieldy armies on the atrocious roads of medieval Europe. It had become necessary for armies to transport a great quantity of cannon, and cannon could not be made on the spot out of local timber, in the same way as catapults and trebuchets. The gradual evolution of the gun-carriage over the fourteenth and fifteenth centuries solved the problem only so long as the state of the roads permitted heavy traffic. Though vast siege-trains stupefied contemporaries with their strength and armament, cannon frequently had to be hauled into awkward positions, and they were prone to getting bogged down or falling into ditches.

Ramelli says that he made use of this particular instrument in various places, and found it very much to the purpose. 'It is a very convenient device to transport artillery easily in high and mountainous places: for in such a case, the horses, through their hard and laborious efforts, might not have the strength to cope with such a great strain, and might fail to reach our destination.' The instrument is quite simple, however. It is in the form of a portable winch with claw-like legs which get a grip on the surface of the road, and which fold into each other when not in use. The drum of the winch acts as a support for a pulley through which a rope attached to the gun-carriage can be passed. This rope can be drawn downhill by a team of horses. A second rope is attached to the winch, passed through a second pulley on the gun-carriage, and drawn uphill by a second team. In this way two teams of horses can put their strength into a task without obstructing each other.

(*Zonca, p. 26*)

'Those types of Mills, which have their Motion from the power of animate bodies, are of three kinds, one when the motor, through the greater radius of the lever, moves its weight directly towards the centre of the world, as it would be when the motors ascending the circumference of the wheel from within, make them turn. The second sort is when the motors themselves walk outside the circumference of the wheel, which stands parallel to the surface of the earth. The third kind is the one, whose motor will walk almost in the same manner, through the plane of the horizon, except that this plane has a little incline, which serves to give impetus to the motion of the men or animals that move them, whence it happens that they are somewhat faster than the aforesaid types, as can be seen in the drawing of this present mill, which grinds corn in the city of Venice most effectively. Half way up is the wheel, in diameter twenty-one feet, which will make quite a gentle incline for the animals to walk on: but they suffer great fatigue in this, because while they walk, the wheel gives way to them, and they stay in the same place, and so get very tired; whence it is necessary to have two pairs, to be changed every two hours, so that two can rest each time during this period. The wheel has a wall on one side, so that the animals should not be frightened by the height. The axle has its upper pivot of wood, and at the bottom one of iron carried in a bronze support, which is to carry the whole burden of the weight, for iron wears with bronze, as steel with brass.

'I should like to add the use which is derived from such mills, and likewise the expense you are put to in erecting them, for the benefit of all who have a concern or delight in such things, so that they can increase or reduce the parts, at their pleasure.

'The experts say such a mill could cost about 400 scudi. Two pairs of Bovine animals are kept, which are changed, as I said, two every two hours. They eat a cartload of hay in 20 days, so that reckoning the cost of the beasts, that of the Duty, and that of the Miller, it costs one sequin a day.

'Ten Venetian stara[1] of corn are ground in a day, and the Miller gets for his pay, 1 libra 10 soldi, and 3 pounds of flour in the staro.'

(ZONCA, New Theatre of Machines, 1607)

[1] About 6⅔ English bushels, according to a contemporary English traveller.

DESPITE THE SPREAD OF WATERMILLS AND WINDMILLS, MANY DISTRICTS HAD TO rely upon animals for power, because these were more reliable than the temperamental elements. Much of the industry of Europe continued to derive its power from 'animate bodies'. The original type is the treadmill, in which the motors – men, donkeys, or dogs – climb the circumference of a vertical wheel. In the second the beast, usually blindfolded, walks in a circle around the mill. The third differs only in having an inclined ramp.

(Zonca)

CONTEMPORARY ACCOUNTS DESCRIBE SMALL PORTABLE MILLS USED IN BESIEGED castles or in ships at sea. But a mobile mill for an army on the march, and conveniently operated by the horses whose task it is to haul it in the baggage-train, is a new conception. The compact structure of the mill displays the ingenuity of its inventor at a time when the work of military engineers was vitiated by unnecessary intricacy. The crossbar, which in transit is slung at the side of the carriage, fixes on to the central bar, and revolves the large wheel below it. The rungs on the wheels engage in spur-gears on either side, and these drive the millstones in the two hutch-like housings.

The Dutch War of Independence is distinguished by the scorched – or drowned – earth policy adopted by the Dutch. The Spanish army countered by endeavouring to make themselves independent of local produce. Sixty mills of this sort suggest an ambitious project rather than a freak device to be admired. But although the notion won fame for Targone, it did not prosper. Presumably, if an army could not live off the land, the best alternative was to transport grain which had already been processed into flour.

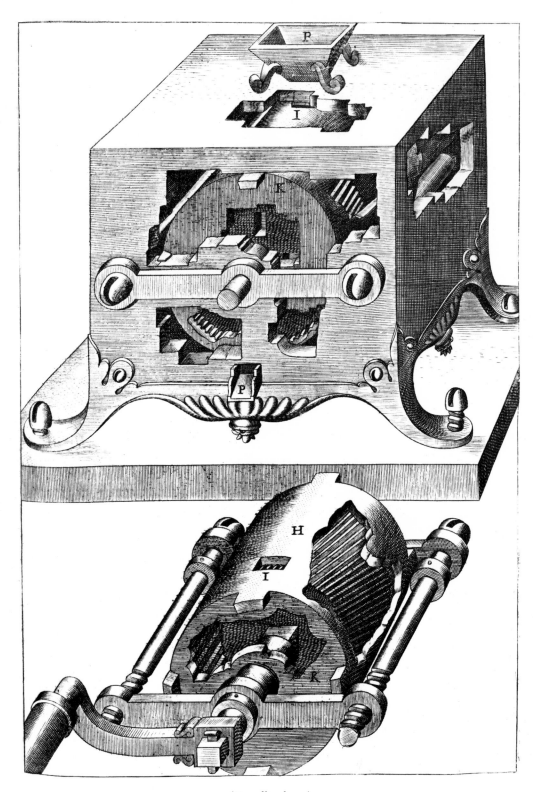

(*Ramelli, pl. 129*)

THE DESIGN OF HAND-MILLS WAS A POPULAR OUTLET FOR THE MECHANICAL IN-genuity of Renaissance inventors. These were practical inventions, yet they allowed scope for subtle work-manship and demanded great precision. This was an age of constant warfare in which sieges alternated with mobile campaigns, and portable mills would come in useful, since they could be used by military units when watermills or windmills were inaccessible. Turriano, the most famous engineer of the time, fashioned one for the Emperor Charles V 'of most subtle work and smallness that a monk could easily hide it in his sleeve: yet it would abundantly serve eight persons for their day's allowance'. Another engineer reports: 'I believe I have learnt how to make the little mill. It is but 2 inches in diameter, yet it will grind 16 lb. an hour: of this I have seen the proof.' The first reference to hand-mills, however, is much earlier, because King Edward III sent some to his three sons when they were campaigning in the south of France about 1370.

Ramelli has offset the central drum slightly, so that the grain falling freely into the wider section will be compressed and more easily ground. He used this scheme in some of his waterwheels. The helical grooves on the grinding surface of both drum and casings, allied with the compactness of the instrument, make this one of Ramelli's most attractive designs. No doubt the drawing was done from the original model. The various split-head screws and flanges, more clearly seen in the lower picture, demonstrate the ease with which the machine may be dismantled and reassembled whenever necessary.

(*Ramelli, pl. 152*)

'Another sort of bridge by which one can cross the water in the moat of a town, or fortress, very convemiently. First the bridge is taken on four cart wheels as far as the counterscarp, then the wheels are removed and replaced by four smaller ones. . . . This bridge is made in the manner that you see in the drawing, closed and well shut in, like a boat, in order that the water may not penetrate, but it has a broad base, so as to hold up better on the water. Besides it has at the back a rudder, like those of barges, with which it is steered, and on each side two wheels, which serve as oars, turning by means of a handle with the force of a man who stands in the bridge, without being seen or attacked by anyone. Apart from this, four or six arquebusiers are posted in the bridge at the head of it, who with arquebuses or muskets prevent the enemy from attacking them when the bridge reaches the bank of the moat. The time being come . . . it is pushed into the water with levers . . . and so it goes on constantly trying to join one bridge with the other sufficient for the width of the moat; the soldiers may then cross very conveniently, above and within.'

(RAMELLI, *Various Ingenious Machines*, 1558)

FEW NOTIONS OCCUPIED THE MINDS OF EARLY INVENTORS AND MECHANICIANS AS much as the possibility of creating a self-propelled armoured carriage. Authors of contemporary manuscripts frequently propounded more than one theory by which such a carnage could work. Therefore, strictly speaking, no one invented the tank, because the idea was always there; the question was who would first produce a workable model. Until the introduction of the internal combustion engine all these projects broke down on the question of power. In 1335 Guido da Vigevano produced a windmill-tank, and his principles were adopted by successors whose inventions, however, were too slow to be used in action. Man-powered carriages involved an amount of labour which was far from being commensurate with results. However, it was realized that though armoured cars were unsuitable for a war of movement, they could at least be pressed into service as bridges. Normally when a commander was faced with a river or moat he ordered a pontoon bridge to be constructed. But Guido had devised a self-propelled pontoon which could function on water. His boats, similar to Ramelli's, are driven by a man turning a crankshaft which sets a pair of paddle-wheels in motion. It may well have been the model for all those which appeared in subsequent books on the art of war, at least until Ramelli's time. Guido's version is neater than Ramelli's, although it did not occur to him to add the little wheels for climbing the opposite bank, nor ordinary cartwheels for overland travel. With such a long tradition behind them, paddles must have provided the obvious solution. The earliest steam-driven boats also applied that principle of propulsion. Indeed it has survived to this day – upon the boating lakes of children's playgrounds.

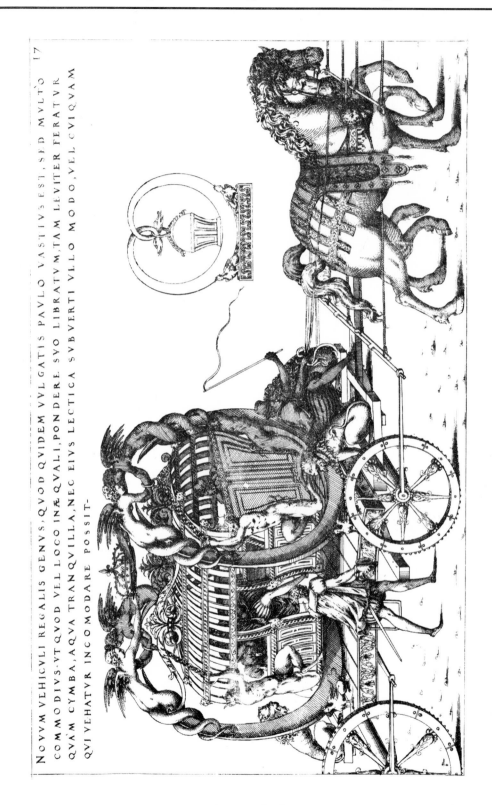

(*Besson, pl. 17*)

THE DESIRE OF THEIR CREATORS TO PRODUCE THE ILLUSION THAT THE WORLD OF fantasy had come to life frequently made sixteenth-century machines seem more complicated than they in fact were. The triumphal chariots of Renaissance pageants, familiar from a great many paintings and tapestries, are a good example, because here the supernatural figures of mythology can be seen performing their supernatural deeds, the secret of which is known only to the designer. It was natural for Besson, when designing a royal coach, to allow full play for imagination, and to obscure the mechanical side of the design with an artist's exuberance. For behind the riot of grotesque imagery, and the apparently undisciplined confusion of baroque figures, there lies a very simple principle. All the grovelling satyrs, the crouching harpies, the roaring lions and bizarre winged maidens equipped with fish-tails serve only to conceal the means whereby 'in any uneven place it will level itself out, like a ship in calm water, and the carriage cannot be overturned, nor those who travel within be harmed in any way'. It is fortunate that a simpler diagram has been inset in the picture, so that the new device can be recognized as similar to a common hammock, with the carriage swinging from iron rings suspended from the arms of the serpent-women who adorn the upper part of the circular frame. The rings are hung from their interlocked arms so that these will take the strain by pushing the heads of the figures together, thus dividing the pressure between two points. The satyrs are part of the carriage, but they could equally well be replaced by pegs. The harpies support the base of the circle. The lions just roar, and add to the marvel.

There is a legend that the hammock was first introduced to France a couple of years later, at the siege of Sancerre, not far from Orléans, where Besson was teaching. It is said that a Huguenot, who had served in Brazil as a soldier of fortune, had learned the custom from the Indians. It could have been that Besson was told of the hammock some time earlier by this man, and realized that that suspension had other potentialities. It is known that he had an early interest in suspension, but this was by no means unique to him, in view of the appalling condition of sixteenth-century roads. His carriage, however, has an additional artifice: it is carried not by axles but by a central shaft which is attached to the four wheels, so that the whole coach turns in a single movement. We are informed that 'the carriage being perfectly balanced on itself, even if two of the wheels should fall off, no harm will come of it'.

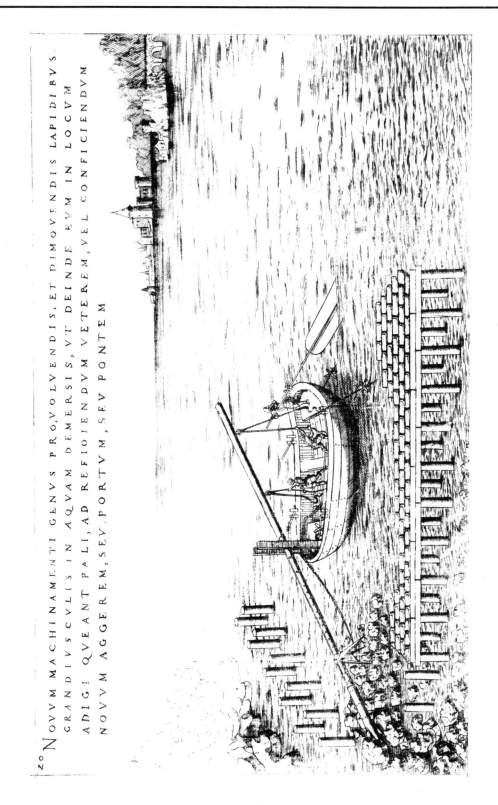

(*Besson, pl. 20*)

'If anything be buried and fixed in the stream so as to spoil the navigation, besides the common machines used by workmen for removing such obstructions . . . (there are various other methods) . . . you may also fetch it up from the bottom where the sea is shallow by the following contrivance. You must have two smacks, like those of fishermen: in the stern of one of these, you must have an axis upon which a very long pole must swing like the beam of a balance: to that end of the pole which lies out from the stern you must fasten a shovel, three foot broad and six long. By lowering this shovel you scoop up the mud, and so throw it into the other smack which lies by for that purpose.'

(LEON BATTISTA ALBERTI, *On Architecture*, 1452)

BESSON'S DEVICE SHOWN HERE WAS NO INNOVATION. ALBERTI IS DESCRIBING A giant spoon for ladling mud from the bottom and, since Besson makes no mention of any such thing, it is curious that both Beroalde and Pascali (a later commentator on Besson's book) speak of the beam having a spoon or cupped shovel. This implement must have been quite common in the century following Alberti's work, for his French translator, Jean Martin, mentions the 'mud-shovel (*pelle a bourbe*), as our workmen call it'. This was years before Besson. However, in addition to the constant problem of dredging, the builder of a mole or the creator of a new port such as Le Havre, which was founded about this time, might also have had to face the special problem of removing rocks from the entrance to what would be the harbour, or where they obstructed pile-driving operations. Besson therefore replaced the shovel by a three-pronged fork which could grasp a rock, and suspended a tripod from the beam, to serve as an adjustable fulcrum for the lever. The holes in the beam show that the tripod could be pegged in wherever there was a suitable foundation on which it could bear. The rope is for retracting the tripod when it is being moved into position and might catch on some projecting rock. The enormous paddle enables the workmen to swing the boat from side to side, thus applying leverage on the obstruction in a lateral as well as a vertical direction. It seems as though the three-pronged form captivated Besson. Three-pronged anchors can be seen at each side, stuck in the bed of the sea, backed by crossbars for protection against unwanted drift.

41. MACHINA FVNDVM MARIS PVRGANS.

(*Verantius, pl. 41*)

'The cities which enjoy the benefit of navigable ports, being much privileged by nature with the convenience and common benefit that is drawn thereby, yet it is very necessary that such a convenience be preserved and increased, especially in preserving the depth of the water so that shipping can stay there not only comfortably but safely, and therefore it is necessary to construct good instruments for this purpose. . . .'

(BUONAIUTO LORINI, *On Fortifications*, 1596)

VERANTIUS AND LORINI AGREE THAT THEIR DREDGERS WERE MODIFIED VERSIONS – improved ones, admittedly – of those already functioning in the canals and lagoons of Venice. Quite a few ports became completely silted up in the Middle Ages. Moreover, as ships became too large for the shallow waters which had hitherto given them harbourage, many more ports remained serviceable for fishing boats and barges only.

Solutions were various. Early in the fifteenth century a small boat was used to drag a giant rake across the stretch to be cleared. Besson illustrates something similar, in the form of a great curved rake attached to a raft which in turn can be operated from the shore by winches. Alberti, more simply, suggests oyster nets. The modern method of an endless chain made its appearance in the sixteenth century, witness Brueghel's drawing of a dredger at work on a Dutch canal in 1561. Verantius adds in his commentary that 'in rivers which are not too deep, another sort of machine can be used: two waterwheels are placed on each side of a barge, attached to an axle placed across it. To this axle you can fix some large hollow paddles, which in turn break up the riverbed, and raise the sand and mud.'

This practice, however, proved inadequate for operations in deep water, so that modifications had to be made. Therefore the present drawing shows a shovel lowered from pulleys by the action of a treadwheel. (Verantius was inordinately proud of having designed a treadwheel worked from its outer rim, rather than by climbing up the inner wall, and he employs this method whenever he has the slightest excuse.) The winches then close the shovel in a simple scissors action. Lorini suggests a similar machine, though he makes no claim to have altered the common dredger except in respect of the shape of the shovel, which, however, does not close so tightly as in Verantius' design.

(*Besson, pl. 58*)

'About the time that the Emperor Charles V was planning his second African expedition, another most ingenious man was sent in to his chamber, who showed the Emperor an instrument, strongly and cunningly made, and twisted round in a circle, whereby whole sunken warships might be drawn up out of the sea, all in one piece. He demonstrated how ten thousand-weight can be raised high above the ground when an iron axle is slightly twisted round in a circular movement by the lightest pressure of a man's fingers. But the Emperor, partly for fear of the expense, partly frightened by the growing size of the proportion (which he thought would be unequal to the weight to be raised), treated him generously and sent him back to Germany.'

(ZENOCARUS, *Life and Deeds of the Emperor Charles V*)

OF ALL THE ACHIEVEMENTS OF ANCIENT ENGINEERING, THERE WERE FEW THAT caught the imagination of the Renaissance so strongly as the famous occasion when with one hand Archimedes drew a ship out of the harbour, as though it were a horse at the end of a rein. The raising of sunken ships provided opportunities for emulating Archimedes and at the same time performing a useful service. Accordingly it became a very popular undertaking, though would-be salvage men were not particularly successful in their operations. About the time when Charles was preparing his expedition, a ship went down at the entrance to the Venetian lagoon in only 'five paces of water', yet it could not be raised, despite the efforts of the Venetian Government and the owners of the vessel. When the same thing happened in 1550, in less than four paces of water 'so that the prow, poop and a great part of the lower decks were above the surface of the water', the authorities despaired, and ordered that the ship be broken up, for fear that it might block the entrance to the lagoon. This incident inspired Niccoló Tartaglia to write his treatise, 'The Troublesome Invention', to demonstrate that not only could sunken ships be raised, but even a 'solid tower of metal'. His method involved filling salvage ships with water, making fast to the wreck, and at low tide pumping out the water. Winches and pulleys would raise the wreck still further, and the rising tide was expected to complete the salvage work.

Besson relied more on his power engine. In the same way as Charles V's engineer, he was entranced by the potentialities of worm-gear, then known by the magical-sounding name of 'perpetual screw'. This drawing follows almost immediately after an imaginative sketch showing how he thought Archimedes had pulled that ship out of the harbour by means of such a perpetual screw. The peculiar 'gearboxes' on the salvage ships are in fact pairs of worm-gears held in a wooden frame. Each pair turns one winch. Besson claims that this will raise a boat from any depth less than 30 fathoms. But perhaps he should have provided diving bells for his salvage men, as Tartaglia did. They could not be expected to tie knots at such depths.

(Ramelli, pls. 155, 156)

'And also there is devised a certaine Engine, that goeth some with a screwe and some with a nut uppon teeth, that you may lift up the side of a whole double Cannon, setting it up under the Axletree, and so you may take off the wheele of the cannon, & these be very much used in Germany & in Dutchland, to lift up the side of a great Dutch wagon when that it is laden.'
(WILLIAM BOURNE, *Rare Inventions and Strange Devises*, The 57 Devise, 1578)

THE SCREWJACK, INVENTED TO SERVE THE SAME PURPOSE FOR WHICH IT IS STILL employed – to assist the removal of wheels of carriages and wagons – was soon applied less worthily. Ramelli was not satisfied with its exclusive use with artillery, and says 'The operation to be performed with this present machine, is that one man alone shall lift a door off its hinges very easily and with little noise.' The second picture shows this man at work, with an officer standing by to give him orders. In practice, it is difficult to believe that it would be possible to carry such a cumbersome machine to the city gates by stealth, as seems from the second illustration to be the intention, unless there were more than the usual taint of treason. It would be easier to bring it into action from outside, under cover of darkness. This would prevent the gate from falling on the operators of the jack. But perhaps the operation has been illustrated the wrong way round for the sake of clearer exposition of its action.

We owe the first illustration, so precise that it could be derived from a catalogue of only half a century ago, to such abuses of the jack. Tools designed for honest work have disappeared with little more than bare mention, and their history has to be reconstructed from hints and insufficient descriptions. The military screwjack survives not only in the present superb illustration but in at least one other example – richly decorated like all the implements of war prepared by German armourers for princely use – which until the Second World War was to be found in the Schlossmuseum in Berlin. Although this was a screwjack, similar to Ramelli's, another type, the ratchet-jack 'which goeth with a nut upon teeth', appeared about the same time. This device seems to have been rather more common. In 1566 an Austrian nobleman demonstrated to King Charles IX of France an engine 'whereby the said King, when he was but xvi years of age,

lyfted from the ground a great weight, which the strongest man in his court was not able to remove'. John Dee also tells of the 'Dutch Waggon Racke', by means of which a solitary man could hold up a heavily laden wagon. In both these instances the implement is compared to the mechanism of a crossbow rack. Probably the reference is to a crannequin, in which the crank, pinion, and ratchet combined to draw the bowstring. Crannequins were in general use, and are to be found in many present-day collections of armour. They may have popularized the rack-and-pinion principle. Sooner or later, however, this mechanism was bound to be adapted to pushing as well as pulling. Here the usages of peace borrowed from those of war. The new modifications to the jack included the shoe, which enables force to be applied when it is impossible to insert the whole jack under the load, as well as the worm-gear and crank-handle, both of which likewise make for compactness. Ancient and medieval jacks were turned by capstan-bars. Their use was limited, so that this little hand jack may be regarded as an invention of the Renaissance.

(*Ramelli, pls. 157, 158*)

'In as much as Mirebel, a Protestant town, is close to Ville-neuve, whose interior they could see, through being higher up, the refugees from Ville-neuve had the greater desire to return there, and they would have undertaken it, but the doubtful outcome at Sommieres delayed them. At this stage a lock-smith soldier who had come from the town assured La Pradelle, the Protestant general, of the means of taking it by surprise. Under the walls of the town, there is a barred gate of iron trellis-work, where the rain-water flows out of the town, which he promised to tear away, and be the first to enter.'

(LA POPELINIERE'S *History of France*, 1581)

DURING THE FRENCH WARS OF RELIGION, IN WHICH RAMELLI SERVED, MORE THAN one city was captured by an advance party which had rowed up to the sewer gate at night and broken it open. In this way it had been possible to penetrate into the heart of the town, and seize control before being detected. Ramelli would have known of such captures by surprise. He describes a rich assortment of engines for breaking and entering, in particular those used for forcing the bars of lattices and gratings 'be it in the wall of a town at the outlet of a conduit, or in some other place'.

The two wrenches illustrated here are his simplest. As in the case of the jacks, they are examples of a new development – the complex tool with adjustable parts – which had, however, existed in comparable form in antiquity. For example, two specimens of a truly terrifying obstetrical instrument used by Roman doctors have been discovered and identified by archaeologists. But generally the tools of almost all the trades

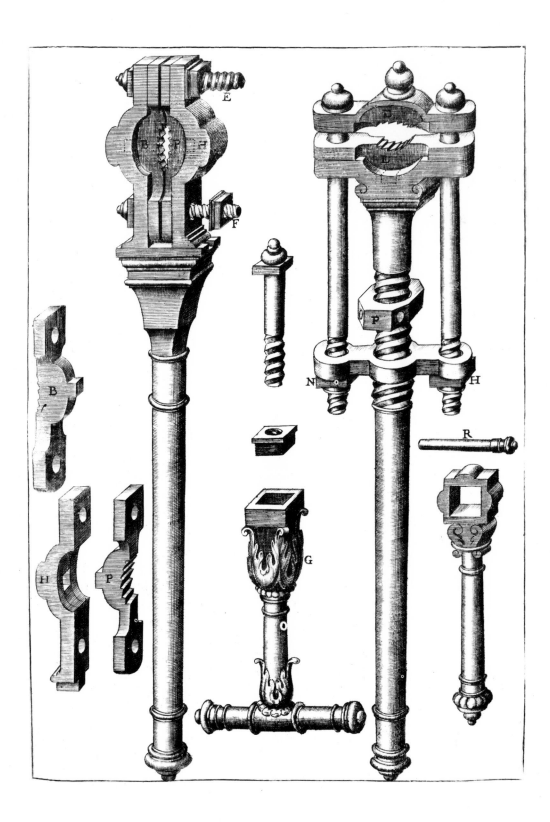

remained simple, and consisted of a handle and some functional extension. Vices were the first adjustable manual tools. Jacks and wrenches followed. About the same time, two other simple tools appeared, and ones which may be said to hold our civilization together: the screwdriver and the spanner. The oldest surviving screwdriver is attached to a suit of armour belonging to the Emperor Maximilian I (1459-1519). As the helmet was fastened to the suit with split-head screws, the emperor when fully armed was literally screwed in. Though the spanners *G* and *R* in Ramelli's picture seem too ornate with their profusion of acanthi and volutes, they are comparatively simple when set against two contemporary spanners which are preserved in the Tower of London, upon which an armourer has lavished all the decorative skill considered proper for instruments of war. Only because of their military association did such tools receive so large a measure of care and attention, and it is for this reason, too, that some have survived until modern times.

The two pieces of iron *B* and *P* mark another interesting development. Imperceptibly the practice had grown up of using a harder material for parts which were subject to the greatest wear, and of making these removable, so that they might be replaced without difficulty. Though Ramelli's drawing is the first clear representation of bearings of this description, he advances no reason why these should be separate from the back piece. It seems as though the development crept up on him unawares.

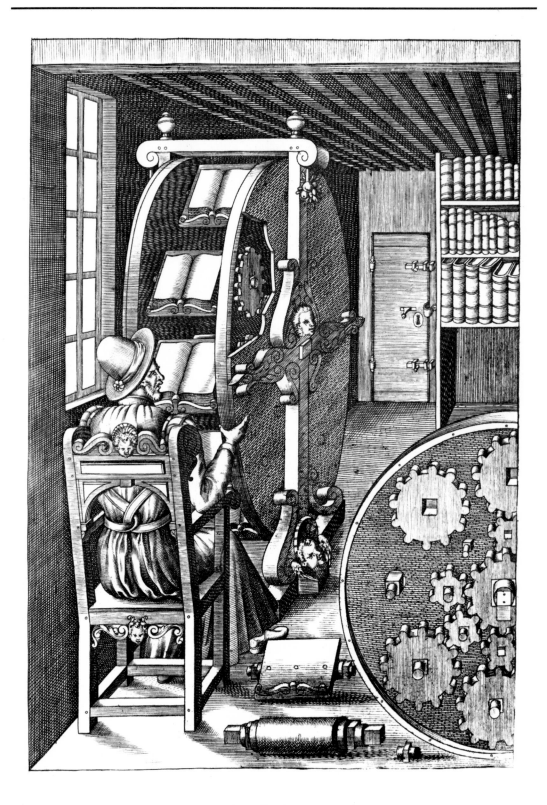

(Ramelli, pl. 188)

'A beautiful and ingenious machine, which is very useful and convenient to every person who takes pleasure in study, especially those who are suffering from indisposition or are subject to gout: for with this sort of machine a man can see and read a great quantity of books, without moving his place: beside, it has this fine convenience, which is, of occupying little space in the place where it is set, as any man of understanding can well appreciate from the drawing.'

(RAMELLI, *Various Ingenious Machines*)

RAMELLI INTRODUCES HIS MECHANICAL READING DESK WITH THESE WORDS. HIS gift to scholarship, however, appears to have gone unremarked, unless it was a remote inspiration for various modern types of rotating filing cabinets. Considering that the wealthier classes were paying increasing attention to physical comfort, it is not surprising that Renaissance carpenters and smiths became interested in applying their inventiveness to domestic furniture. As early as the fifteenth century, desks begin to revolve, lecterns to have adjustable standards, lamps and reading desks to swivel on brackets. By Ramelli's time chairs could be folded into the form of tables, or become step-ladders. Yet the designers of that age retained something of the medieval desire to remain uncluttered. Furniture was intended to be simple and portable, and the saving of space remained an important consideration.

The inset shows the working of the mechanism. As the drum revolves it turns the central gear, which turns the inner circle of smaller gears, and these the outer circle, which finally turns the rollers supporting the bookrests. The idea is that the rollers will keep their axes constantly parallel. It is unfortunate that by including the inner circle of gears, Ramelli has ensured that the rollers will revolve in the same direction as the drum, and the books will fall to the floor.

95

Coperchio de legno foderato de rame

ferro infocato

ferro

legno

Lamina derame

Instrumento da tenere caldi li piedi

(Scappi, pl. 22)

'*A conceipted Chaffingdish to keepe a Dish of meate long hote upon the Table without any coles therein.*

'*Let the Dish be somewhat deepe, and cause the Chafingdish to bee made of such shape as may best receive the same, into the which you may convey a peece of yron red hote, the same beeing of an apte forme to lie in the bottom of the Chafingdish. . . . From this ground did these warming pannes first spring, which . . . being put in their cases, and those cases wrapped in linen bagges, doe serve to heate beddes with, and to cast one into a kindly sweat. The like device is also used by others in conveying of such iron pannes into hollow boxes of wood first lined inwardly with mettall, and iron chests, either to lay under their feete where they use to write or studie in cold weather, or in their coches to keepe their feet warm. The now distressed king of Portugall, caused a paire of wooden soles to bee made for a paire of shoes . . . which he would warme at his pleasure with* Mars *well rubified.*'[1]

(HUGH PLAT'S *Jewel House of Art and Nature*, London, 1594)

[1] Red-hot iron, in the language of the alchemists.

THE DERIVATION FROM CHAFING DISHES THROUGH WARMING PANS DEMONSTRATES how these 'instruments to keepe their feet warm' found their way among the kitchen utensils illustrated in Scappi's cookery book. The association goes beyond their common technical principle whereby the desired heat is obtained by placing red-hot bars inside several layers of insulating material. The interest lies more in the reasons behind the sudden appearance of all three forms of this device, certainly not a complicated machine, and hardly worthy of the name of *instrumento*. Surely they originated from a new demand for physical comfort, refinement and sensitivity: meat must not only be impressively garnished, as in the great banquets of medieval princes, but it must come to the table hot. The masters of splendid but draughty chambers were no longer content to impress their guests with a display of magnificence; they also wanted to keep their feet warm.

These standards of comfort spread rapidly to other classes of society. When foot-warmers first appeared they were for popes and for the kings of Portugal (albeit distressed). Now Plat and his fellows made them available to anyone who could afford the materials from which they were made. The Dutch were the first to take them up on a large scale, as might be expected of the richest and most energetic European nation. By the end of the century, 'the Weomen, as well at home, as in the Churches, to drive away cold, put under them little pannes of fier, covered with boxes of wood, boared full of holes in the top. And this sordid remedy, they carry with them, by the high way in waggons, which the Danes and Muscovites use not, though oppressed with greater cold: only some of the more noble weomen, disliking this remedy, choose rather to weare breeches, to defend them from the cold.'

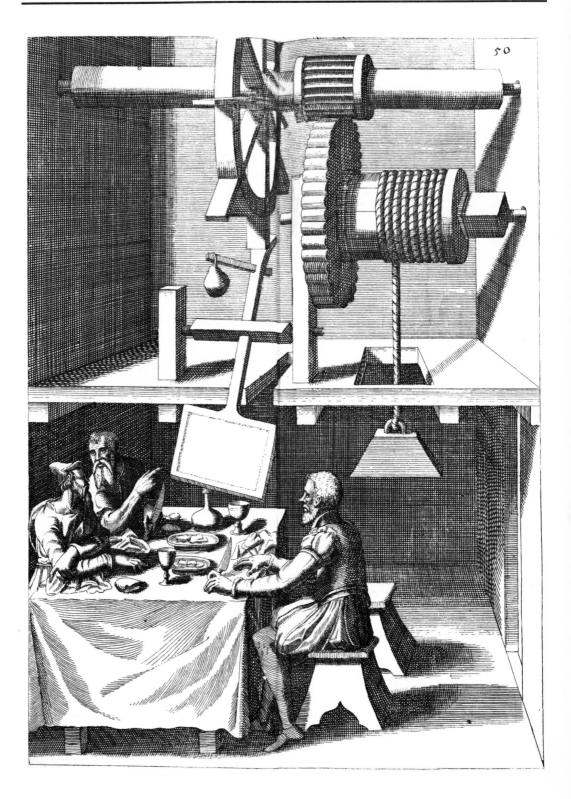

(*Strada, pl. 50*)

IF INGENUITY WAS TO BE APPLIED TO KEEPING WARM IN WINTER, THEN THE LOGICAL development was to devise means of keeping cool in summer. This was taken seriously in Italy, where architects were predisposed towards lavishing their art and expertise on keeping the occupants of houses cool. They worried very little about warmth, and it is probable that the bulky close-fitting clothes of the sixteenth century made the heat of summer much more intolerable than winter cold. Certainly all the architectural handbooks of the period concern themselves a great deal with utilizing breeze and shade. The fashion for fountains, and their extravagant forms, must have been similarly inspired.

Although frequent references are made to it, there is little information about the working of the air-conditioning apparatus in the Villa Trento. It is probable that the caves under the house were first used as a 'grotto' for summer entertainments, until some Trento was inspired to pump the cool air of the cave into a chamber of his villa. The mechanism may have been more elaborate in construction than that which is shown here. A simpler version, to be turned by hand, is illustrated in Agricola's *De Re Metallica*, where it is employed for ventilating a mine. The motive force, once again, is derived from the clock. A falling weight revolves the spur-gear and pinion; and this in turn revolves the wheel with its projecting paddles. The assumption is that there is some means of winding up the weight. As the paddles revolve, each in turn will strike the handle of 'a square frame with a stiff piece of cloth, or other inner part, drawn tight across, like the sail of a ship'. When this frame is released, the counter-weight hanging from the crossbar will swing it against the next paddle. In view of its action as a brake on the entire machine, the fan will move slowly, but it must have some effect, and the guests are presumably frozen – if only in wonder at their host's ingenuity.

(Besson, pl. 52)

'Here . . . I set before your eyes a type of a squirt which hath bene devised to cast much water upon a burning house, wishing a like squirt and plenty of water to be alwaies in a readinesse where fire may do harme, for this kind of squirt may be made to holde an hoggeshed of water, or if you will a greater quantity thereof, and may so be placed on his frame, that with ease and a small strength, it shall be mounted, imbased, or turned to any one side right against any fired marke, and made out to squirt out his water with great violence upon the fire that is to be quenched.'

(CYPRIAN LUCAR, *A Treatise named Lucarsolace*, London, 1592)

FIVE ILLUSTRATIONS FROM BESSON'S BOOK APPEAR IN *Lucarsolace*, ONE OF THOSE COL-lections of applied mathematics which became increasingly popular in Elizabethan England, and which helped to popularize the ideas and projects of Besson and his fellows. The fire engine described here is among the drawings Lucar selected for reproduction.

With uncharacteristic modesty, Besson says of his fire engine that he thinks such machines are not yet known. But in fact this does seem to be the first practical fire engine; except for a few Greek drawings, previous generations had to be content with buckets of water and a human chain. These little fire engines mounted on trolleys became quite common during the next century. Usually they incorporated the ancient idea of a pump with two containers of water and operated alternately by a lever and a squirt. Besson's engine is based on the principle of a syringe, such as was traditionally used in the practice of medicine. However, just as he tends to do with his other devices, he blunts the effect of a good idea by failing to notice how slowly his machine will operate. In order to force the plunger home and eject a single jet, the screw must be fully turned, and then it must be unwound to allow the container to be refilled. All the same, when it was working at last, quite a fine jet could be brought to play on the fire, and from a further distance than the contents of a bucket could be thrown. This, as Besson points out, will be useful when the flames are so strong that it is impossible to approach the burning building.

46. Sawmill

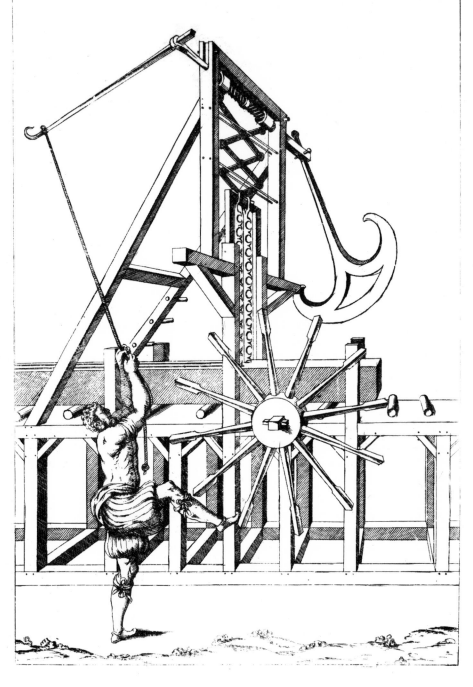

(Besson, pl. 14)

AN ENGLISH TRAVELLER IN 1593 OBSERVED THAT AMONG THE WONDERFUL SIGHTS OF Danzig there was a mill which 'without any help of hand, saweth boards, having an iron wheele, which doth not only drive the saw, but hooketh in, and turneth the boards to the saw'.

It was no great problem for the medieval carpenter to apply the principles of a waterwheel to the simple reciprocal action of a saw. By Besson's time water-powered sawmills were common in Europe. Some designers also saw an opportunity for making an additional saving by automatic feed. By attaching the timber to the axle of the wheel it would be propelled into the teeth of the saw. The Danzig hook appears less prone to slipping than Besson's rollers, or the carriage depicted in a water-powered sawmill of Ramelli.

Besson was aware of this, and somewhat lamely explains that his saws would be very useful 'where there is a shortage of water and in a low place where the timber can be drawn straight down to the machine'. It is clear that in this instance necessity was not the mother of invention. Besson was more interested in what he terms the 'mathematical explanation' for its own sake. Since sawing was an ancillary trade of architecture, it had its attractions for the Renaissance engineer. Machines for cutting wood or marble are quite common. But in this example the originator has moved far from the purely functional. In his commentary Beroalde underlines the importance of maintaining the great anchor-shaped counterpoise at exactly right-angles to the bar which drives it. When the counterpoise has swung through 90 degrees, Besson appears to assume that the nuts on the axle will move towards the centre through several turns of the thread, and that the counterpoise will then swing back and drive them apart. He then uses another of his pet devices, 'popularly known as a happevilain' – the crookcatcher – but for which Beroalde proposes the more refined name of 'grasshopper'. This consists of folding scissors which pull the saw up and down as they open and close. Meanwhile the sawyer, who has to use both his hands on the driving bar, kicks the capstan round with his foot, so as to turn the rollers which feed the wood into the saw. It is not surprising that Beroalde remarks that German sawmills differ considerably from this. The artist, less optimistic than Besson about one man's capacity for doing the work of eight, has shown the operator without his shirt.

(Strada, pl. 62)

ZONCA SAYS OF THE SILK SPINNER: 'HERE ARE SEEN SO MANY MOVEMENTS OF WHEELS, shafts, pulleys and other sorts of timbers, that the eye is dazzled at thinking how human wits have been able to understand such a variety of things, so many contrary motions, moved by a single wheel.' It is the same here: so many contrary motions, indeed – and all driven by the one poor old fellow in the corner. At the end of all this there is a chain of pots – the oldest water-raising system in the world, well known to the ancient Egyptians. At the other end the operation starts with a device which was original, though not labour-saving. This is a treadwheel modelled on a crown-wheel, in which the unfortunate labourer grasps two of the projecting pegs at the same time as he kicks two more down with his feet. He is seen to be climbing the treadwheel, rather as though he were pedalling a bicycle. If Strada had carried the idea a little further he might have been led to inventing the pennyfarthing bicycle. As his wheel revolves it turns the pinion, which engages the spur-gear, which turns the second pinion, which turns the crown-wheel, which turns the big pinion (immediately below the flywheel), which turns the fourth pinion. All this, of course, has little function except to dazzle the onlooker with the inventor's ingenuity, and to provide space for an extra fly-wheel. The last pinion drives a second crown-wheel which raises the chain of pots. As the main shaft revolves, it winds up the weight, and it is apparent that this is another engine which has been inspired by the mechanism of a clock. As the weight falls, the entire mechanism will engage in reverse gear, while continuing to raise water, 'no hand of man being near', while the little cyclist rests. The apparatus at his back is obviously adapted from the escapement of early clocks. Although a little vague here, it is evident from other pictures in Strada's book that there should be a pallet on the shaft. As the weighted beam oscillates, this should engage with the crown-wheel fitting into the main spur-gear. Not only would this slow down the drop of the weight, but also the raising of the water.

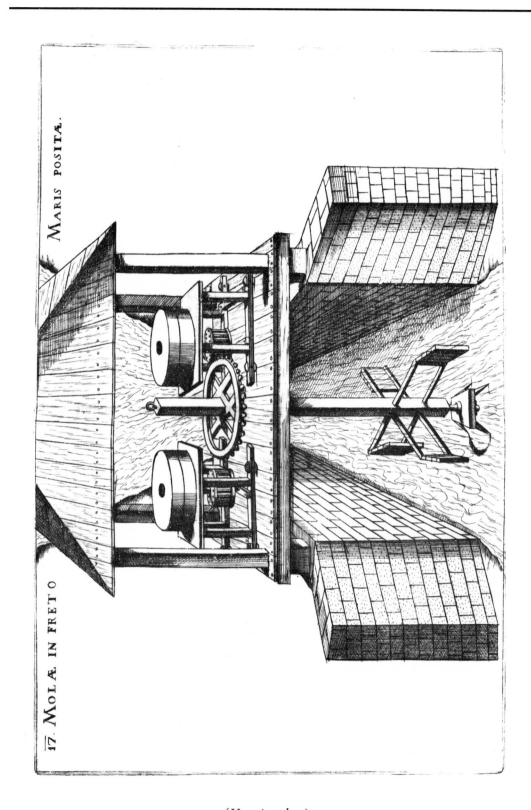

(*Verantius, pl. 17*)

'Has it ever been possible until this hour to put a yoke on the sea, so that it may turn millstones, and serve for other operations which have need of motion? We judge that it can be done, although not every where, but only in narrow and confined places.'

NEW METHODS OF APPLYING MUSCLE-POWER TO THE PROBLEMS OF THE LAND WERE not enough: mechanicians began to explore the potentialities of wind and water. Verantius's idea of placing a mill on some narrow coastal strait presumably was suggested by tide-mills, such as for some centuries had been in use on the Venetian lagoons, and along the coast of the English Channel. Domesday Book records that 'at the entry of Dover Harbour, there is a mill, which batters nearly every ship by greatly disturbing the water, and does great harm to the King and to all men'.

In commenting on his mill, Verantius mentions a similar idea in the form of a reservoir which is filled by the tide and empties with it, turning millwheels at each phase. However, 'it could more suitably be applied on the Ocean, since its ebb and flow is much greater than in the inner seas'. As with many of his proposals, the sea-mill demonstrates that this inventor's willingness to experiment is stronger than his sense of realism. There might be a rocky crevice into which the sea flows with far greater force than any stream which turns a waterwheel, but such a place is unlikely to be accessible to the miller or convenient to his customers. Yet credit is due to Verantius for the boldness of his concept, symbolic of a new and lively search for fresh sources of power.

In the vanes of his waterwheel he has adopted hinges similar to those used in one of his horizontal windmills. Only one side, therefore, will catch the force of the water, while the other is pushed back against its frame. This is an artful idea, but one which greatly reduces the effective area on which wind or water could· be brought to bear.

36 PONS VNIVS FVNIS

(Verantius, pl. 36)

'*Here we passed to the West side of this so famous River Tyber, where of old the Emperour Augustus built a stately bridge: but now men and horses passe in a ferryboate, which is drawne over with the force of men's hands, by a great cable fastned a-crosse the River. And least the boats should be carried away with the swift streame, a second cable is fastned across the River by postes on each side higher than a man: and they have a short cable, to the one end thereof the boat is fastned, and the other end hath a strong wheele, which is put upon the second high cable, upon which the boat slips forward, as it is draune with mens hands by the first low cable: for the Tyber . . . falling here with great force would carry away any boat rowed with oares.*'

(FYNES MORYSON'S *Itinerary*)

VERANTIUS'S CABLE-CAR MAY WELL DERIVE FROM THESE FERRIES, WHICH ARE described by several visitors to Italy. The principle upon which they work is another form of the endless chain of pots. But in this instance the chain is a cord, and there is a single pot: the car. A cable-car of this type figures in a late medieval manuscript, where it is shown carrying baskets of earth for use in the construction of a castle. A similar chain of baskets is likewise described by Lorini, the military engineer, in his book. However, human beings were not yet ready to entrust themselves to a chain of baskets, and the elevator and the funicular railway were still in the future.

The Tiber ferry operated on an almost identical system of chains, though these were parallel to the ground instead of at an angle to it. Verantius suspends his boat and cables on high posts, for little apparent reason except to give passengers the thrill of riding high through the air. It is difficult to see any advantage in raising his 'bridge' high above the water, unless the stream were indeed 'falling at great force' or the steepness of the banks created a problem.

The heavy cable supports the car and, as it passes through the block, serves as a line along which the pulleys may glide; otherwise they would slip sideways. The function of the endless chain is performed by the thinner rope, to which the pulleys are attached. As the operator hauls on this, knots, pulleys and car ride towards the posts on the opposite bank.

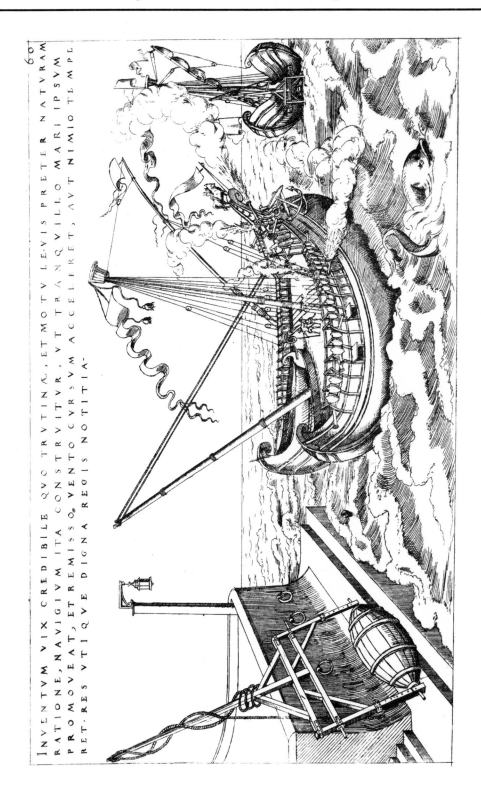

INVENTVM VIX CREDIBILE QVO TRVTINA, ET MOTV LEVIS PRETER NATVRAM RATIONE, NAVIGIVM ITA CONSTRVITVR, VT TRANQVILLO MARI IPSVM PROMOVEAT, ET REMISSO, VENTO CVRSVM ACCELERET, AVT NIMIO TEMPE-RET. RES VTIQVE DIGNA REGIS NOTITIA-

60

(Besson, pl. 60)

'AN INVENTION HARDLY CREDIBLE BY WHICH A SHIP IS SO CONSTRUCTED ON THE principle of the balance and a motion light beyond nature, that it shall move forward in a calm sea, accelerate, when the wind drops, and slow down when there is too much – a matter worthy of the King's notice.' Indeed, this bifurcated ship is barely credible. It is certainly the boldest of Besson's designs. Nowhere else does he reach quite the same height of heroic fantasy. He must have considered it to be his best piece, because it is given the place of honour at the conclusion of the work. Neither could the commentator Beroalde suppress his admiration, while in 1574 Richard Eden, another of those men who presented new inventions to the English public, selected this as one of Besson's most valuable engines when praising him in the dedication to *A very Profitable & Necessary Devise for Navigation.*

It was natural that men of learning anxious to contribute to the common good should be attracted to navigation. Several attempts were made by theorists such as Besson to apply mechanical techniques to the propulsion of ships. One rather misguided humanist designed a quinquereme 'after the true ancient model' for the Venetian Navy, in spite of the opinion of sailors who considered it impossible to place as many as five men to each oar. Its trials proved fairly successful, and delighted those people who saw in it the triumph of learning and science over the crude and outdated traditions of unlettered craftsmen. However, the number of rowers needed caused serious overcrowding. In consequence, there was no proper shelter in bad weather, mortality was heavy, and the 'antique quinquereme' acquired the reputation of a floating pest-house. Other inventors proposed driving their ships by paddle-wheels. The Spaniards tried this experiment in 1540 at Malaga. It worked quite well, and the ship proved capable of turning about much more neatly than an oar-driven galley. Unfortunately it entailed even harder effort than rowing.

Presumably Besson never tried out his ship. As with these others, it employs manual power only and, with outrageous simplification, ignores every move except the first. The windlass on deck, next to the cannon, retracts the lever, which then acts as a gigantic oar operating what Beroalde pompously terms 'the spherical rhombus' so that it functions in the same manner as the blade of an oar. He does not explain how it is returned to position for the next stroke.

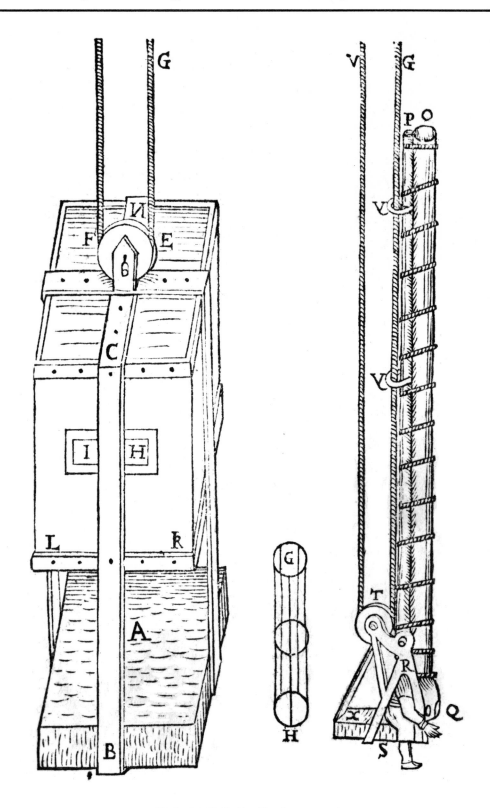

(*B. Lorini*, Delle Fortificatione, *p. 204*)

'In the yeare 1538 in Toledo a citie of Spayne, in the most swyft river Tagus . . . I with twelve thousand other persons, saw in the presence of Charles the Emperour, the fyfth of that name . . . two Greekes: who takyng a chaulderon of greate capacitie, and the mouth turned downwards, and so hanging in the aire by ropes, they fasten certayne postes and boordes in the middest of the chauldron where they place themselves. . . . Then to make it hang equally, they compass the border thereof with leaden plummets on every side equally. . . . The chaldron thus prepared may be fayre and softly let doune into the water. . . . So the men there enclosed, shall so long remayne drye in the myddest of the water, untill success of tyme doo by respiration, debilitate and consume the inclosed ayre.'

(JEAN TAISNIER, *A very Profitable & Necessary Devise for Navigation,*
translated by Richard Eden, 1574)

AS THE EXPLORATION OF THE WORLD PROCEEDED, AND HITHERTO UNKNOWN LANDS were discovered almost every year, the men of the early sixteenth century began to dream of conquests under water. Several attempts were made to construct diving bells, and at least four books on military engineering include a section on standing under water. The interest could have been confined to the practical purpose of 'fishing up artillery from the sea, or anything else that may be on sunken ships, tying up these vessels with ropes so as to draw them out of the sea, beside the great convenience and usefulness of fishing corals', as Lorini suggests. Or was there some deeper fascination?

Two methods were in use. One was a diving bell (on the left in Lorini's picture) in which a chest with a glass window *IH* is weighted down by the stone slab *A*, held in the frame of iron bars, and so lowered into the water. The assumption, apparently, is that the divers can enter and leave the diving bell without water seeping into the chamber. As in the 'cauldron' used at Toledo, there is no method of replacing the exhausted air. The diving suit opposite looks slightly safer. The diver rides on the slab *X* held in the frame *RS*. He has a speaking tube and a respiration pipe of leather, reinforced with iron rings. These are bound together and stapled to the rope used for lowering him. The window *Q* appears to be awkwardly placed – even for inspection of the sea-bed at his feet.

A similar helmet must have been worn by another military engineer, Francesco Marchi, when in July 1535 he descended 45 feet into Lake Nemi to inspect the wreck of a Roman ship. He has left a vivid account of his experience, telling how small things appeared large, so that the fish known as *laterini*, though no bigger than a man's little finger, looked as thick as an arm, and three palms long, 'which, if I had not been informed of the said fish, would have made me much afraid, for the great multitude which swarmed about whichever way I turned . . . and as I was without my breeches, they went to attack me in the part you can imagine, and I hit out at them with my hand, but they cared nothing for it, being in their own home.'

In the hope of being able to hear signals from above he refused to plug his ears. In consequence, 'in going under the water I felt a pain in my ears as if a steel needle was going through them'. A blood vessel burst, and blood came out through his mouth and nose 'till my white shirt was all blood, and for twenty days thereafter there was a thundering in my ears every time I set foot on the ground'.

38. HOMO VOLANS.

(*Verantius, pl. 38*)

AS THE VOYAGERS OF THE RENAISSANCE DISCOVERED MORE AND MORE OF THE Earth's surface, the passion to press further and into other elements grew more intense. The fascination of the air and the depths of the sea – unnatural spheres and hostile to Man – was felt throughout the Middle Ages. There are rumours of aspiring aeronauts, in England and as far afield as China, who cast themselves from towers. The generation of Leonardo da Vinci saw several attempts to master the secret of flight. Legend has made a *succès d'estime* out of the failure of Giambattista Danti, who tried to fly across Perugia as part of the wedding celebrations of a local prince. Another contemporary was not so lucky: an alchemist in the employ of the King of Scots threw himself from the battlements of Stirling Castle, and plummeted into the castle's dungheap. He attributed his failure to his unfortunate, though economical, use of hen's feathers rather than those of an eagle, because these inferior feathers, seeking their 'natural place' in the universe, must have had an irresistible attraction for the dungheap, and drew their wearer down with them.

Both these flyers thought in terms of the birdman. Since Nature had not endowed Man with wings, they would construct frames to compensate for the deficiency. However, the structure of the body being what it is, these men were doomed to failure, and were lucky if they got away with no worse harm than a broken leg. It seems that Leonardo was the first to attempt to create a flying machine, rather than transform himself into a bird. He recognized at least one essential point: that because a man could not work up the necessary momentum by flapping his arms, some form of mechanical aid was indispensable. Also the aviator must have a cradle in which to sit while he operated the mechanism.

However, Leonardo appears never to have tested his flying machines. But, in case of emergency in the air, he designed himself a parachute very similar to that of Verantius. Perhaps it is too imaginative to speak, as Verantius does, of a parachute drop as a 'flying man'. Leaping from high buildings would be safer with a parachute, but no great distance could be achieved.

Verantius alone among our authors may have seen some of Leonardo's drawings. If so, it seems strange that he should have preferred to mention this device rather than one of Leonardo's more ambitious aeronautical projects. It could be coincidental that these two men were alone among Renaissance mechanicians to choose this relatively modest solution to the problem of flight. As it happened, no one succeeded in keeping himself airborne until nearly two centuries after Verantius. Yet it is fitting to end this book of the 'mechanical and mathematical engines' of the Renaissance with this venture into flight. The French poet Salluste du Bartas summed up this pioneering spirit when concluding his list of the triumphs of geometry:

> 'Man rashly mounting through the empty skies
> With wanton wings shall cross the Seas wel-nigh
> And (doubtles) if the Geometrician finde
> Another worlde where (to his working minde)
> To place at pleasure and convenience.
> His wondrous engines and rare Instruments,
> Even (like a little God) in time he may
> To some new place transport this World away.'